"I've never enjoyed
kissing you, Wade!"

Vicki swallowed convulsively as she
spoke.

"Liar!" Wade's eyes hardened as he
gripped her shoulders. "I've a fancy to
kiss you now. You're my wife, which
surely gives me the right to do
anything I want with you."

"That's no reason!" Vicki cried
defensively. Fear suddenly raced
through her. To him she was still the
wife who had thwarted his plans
concerning his grandfather—the
wife whose trickery had resulted in a
son he didn't want. This taunting of
her was just another way of exacting
revenge. Apprehensively she shrank
back.

"Please, Wade, let me go," she
pleaded. "You can't go around kissing
people merely on whim!"

"Right now, I'm interested in more
than a few kisses," he said, his breath
warm on her face.

# MARGARET PARGETER

## boomerang bride

*Harlequin Books*

TORONTO • LONDON • LOS ANGELES • AMSTERDAM
SYDNEY • HAMBURG • PARIS • STOCKHOLM • ATHENS • TOKYO

Harlequin Presents edition published September 1981
ISBN 0-373-10453-7

Original hardcover edition published in 1979
by Mills & Boon Limited

Printed in U.S.A.

# CHAPTER ONE

VICKI stretched full length on her narrow bed, trying to focus her tired eyes on the building across the road. She could see only blurred outlines. The curtains hung undrawn on either side of the window, two thin pieces of faded cotton. It must be because the panes hadn't been cleaned properly for days that she wasn't able to see out of them. Windows hazed over so quickly if they didn't get constant attention, and this she hadn't been able to give them since she got ill. It took her all her time looking after Graham.

Restlessly she turned on her side, checking over anxiously to see if he was still sleeping. He was, and she collapsed on to her pillows again. Outside it was cold for October in Melbourne, but her head felt hot, her pillows uncomfortable, and she couldn't find the strength to pound them back into shape. The one sheet covering her felt sticky from her perspiring body and with tearful impatience she thrust it away. Her tummy felt funny. She hoped she wasn't going to be sick again.

She coughed, just once, but it started the pain in her ribs, making her throat dry and increasing the irritation. Quickly she swallowed, attempting to control a continuing desire to cough. Weakly she reached for her glass of water, taking a hasty drink. When the knock came to the door young Graham, in the makeshift cot beside her, stirred restively but didn't wake up.

Pulling herself up on one elbow, Vicki glanced at him apprehensively. Then, as he resumed his contented sucking of one finger, she gave her attention to the door. It could only be Mrs Parkes from the room across the landing. No other tenant in the house ever came near, only

Mrs Parkes because she was old and lonely and often had nothing much to do. Usually Vicki asked her in, but she hoped that tonight, if she pretended to be asleep, Mrs Parkes would go away.

When the knocking continued she decided the woman must want something urgently, yet she wasn't sure if her legs would carry her as far as the door. Swinging herself on to the edge of the bed, Vicki sat staring at it uncertainly. Mrs Parkes was so good, looking after Graham while she was out at work, even if she did charge exorbitantly. The least Vicki felt she could do was to go and see what seemed to be bothering her so much now.

The insistent knocking began again, this time louder. With an unhappy sigh, Vicki struggled into her wrap. 'One moment,' she called, 'I'm coming!'

Mrs Parkes couldn't have heard, because she tried the door. Vicki, forcing her trembling legs to bear her weight, hobbled towards it, casting another anxious glance at her small son. Graham had been sleeping almost as badly as she had lately. For the first time she could remember she felt really cross with Mrs Parkes. If he woke she might never get him back to sleep again.

Slipping the latch, she stooped to release the bolt, pulling the door open a little as she straightened unsteadily. She wasn't prepared to have it almost thrust back into her face. 'Mrs Parkes!' she choked protestingly, nearly losing her balance.

Then her eyes widened, her voice faded; she was unable to speak. The room seemed to be going round and round and she with it, but she knew she didn't move—she couldn't. Because it wasn't Mrs Parkes who stood on the threshold. It was old Graham McLeod and behind him, looking as grimly forbidding as ever, his grandson, Wade McLeod, her husband, whom she hadn't seen, or been in contact with, for over four years.

'Oh, no!' Vicki knew the horrified cry must have come from her own lips, but she was scarcely aware of uttering it. Stumbling backwards, she thrust out both hands defensively, as if attempting by such a helpless gesture to ward off the two men who advanced on her so ruthlessly. Their determination to sweep her out of their way was stamped on their faces, but she could only think of her son. 'No,' she cried again, her voice shaking, 'you can't come in here!'

For all the notice they took she might never have spoken. The old man pushed past her as if she didn't exist, but his grandson's cruelty was more refined. He made no immediate attempt to explore the poverty-stricken room behind her, but lounged his long length against the door, staring at her as hard as she stared at him. But while her surveillance was made up of anguish and shock, his held only cool calculation. If there was a hint of whiteness under the darkness of his tanned skin, she didn't notice.

His eyes raked her from head to toe and he seemed less than impressed by what he saw. 'So,' his voice was as hard as his eyes, 'I've caught up with you at last! The little wife who fled from Baccaroo, who disappeared as surely as if she'd been wiped from the face of the earth.' His tone became almost savage as his glance went to where his grandfather bent silently over the cot. 'Why hadn't you the sense to keep out of my way permanently?'

Vicki shuddered. It was strange how, after all this time, each word he uttered cut her like a knife thrust, but, in the frozen, panic-stricken regions of her body and mind, she could feel no pain. She whispered hoarsely, her face without colour, 'I tried to. And it was you who told me to go. After you found out about—about——'

'The baby?' He might have been talking about any man's child but his own. There was no trace of emotion anywhere about him. His voice was like steel, his powerful body without softness.

Vicki continued to stare at him dumbly, realising he was still her husband, in spite of the years of separation. He had worn that same remote, unforgiving expression on the morning he had found her in the bathroom. He looked older, but otherwise didn't seem to have changed much. His hair was as thick and dark as ever it had been, but now there were streaks of grey at his temples. His mouth looked thinner, as if it had been held too tightly for too long, and there were deep lines etched around it. These could have nothing to do with her. They were maybe not uncommon in men of his age. Vaguely she calculated, sorting it out, as every day of Wade's age seemed to take on a kind of ludicrous importance. He must be around thirty-six or seven; he had been almost thirty-three when she had married him.

'Wade!' A menacing shout removed Wade McLeod's eyes from her, to narrow on the stocky figure of his grandfather. The old man's face was a startling red, his breathing harsh, as though he had been running, but his expression, as he stared at Wade, was alight with triumph. 'Look what I've found here!'

Vicki, her mind having been temporarily blanked of everything but her husband, came suddenly back to earth. 'No!' she cried, as she had done a few moments ago, but with renewed fierceness. Fright giving strength to her weak limbs, she whirled to the side of the cot, facing old man McLeod like a small termagant. 'My son has nothing to do with you. I want you both to get out of here!'

She might never have spoken for all the notice the two men took of her. The old man glanced indifferently at her stark white face before turning back to stare down at the sleeping baby. Wade, by contrast, strolled over, taking his time, as if he couldn't care less what the cot held. Gazing at them wildly, feeling about as defenceless as a small bird against two hovering hawks, Vicki wondered dully how she had ever hoped to escape them. To try and fight the all-powerful McLeods could only be courting disaster, and while Wade could be willing to let his son go, the old man never would. Not now that he had found out about him, the great-grandson he had longed for.

Neither men spoke. Of the two, surprisingly enough, considering what he was, the old man's face was the one which registered emotion. Wade's, Vicki saw, was almost as revealing as stone as he looked down on his own flesh and blood, the living baby he had, unwittingly, helped to make, one dark, passion-filled if loveless night which now seemed so long ago.

Vicki knew she must try and fight them. Whatever happened they mustn't be allowed to take young Graham from her. Desperately she willed some strength into her voice, thrusting the illness which made her so feeble-minded aside. 'I'm not sure what you came for,' she whispered, 'but if you've satisfied your curiosity, will you please go? I haven't been well.'

Old man McLeod spoke first, the vigour in his voice typical of his family and belying his eighty-odd years. He might have been a man ten or even fifteen years younger. He addressed Vicki flatly. 'I've come for my great-grandson, what else! The child you've taken such care to hide from Wade and me!'

She could understand why Wade had never told him, but this brought bitterness rather than gratitude to her heart. 'You can't have him!' She clutched the side of the cot protectively, trying to steady herself so they shouldn't guess how ill she was. Furiously she faced him across it. 'You don't know, anyway, that it is your great-grandchild. You have no proof.'

The only proof they could have, she reasoned, was that which Wade had practically shaken out of her on that last, awful morning. When she had sagged in his biting hands, tears streaming down her shocked, white face. But the information he had gathered then could, for all he knew, have been wrong. Perhaps this was why he had obviously never given the old man so much as a hint, although it had been chiefly because of his grandfther he had wanted no son.

'Proof?' she heard old McLeod laughing without any

humour in his throat. There was only a leer on his dark old face which still held traces of his former handsomeness, the arrogant good looks Wade had inherited along with everything else which made the McLeods what they were today. They had everything but happiness, Vicki thought scornfully, and she wanted her son to have no part of that.

'Proof!' the old man repeated, as if he doubted her sanity. He waved his hand towards the boy in the cot. Graham was beginning to stir, as if in his sleep he sensed an audience. 'Isn't this living proof? Is he not the spitting image of Wade at his age? He's a living, breathing McLeod if ever I saw one. He even sucks the little finger of his right hand, another McLeod habit, girl. I'm so convinced I'm not even going to check his left thigh, where I'm sure I would find the McLeod birthmark.'

Vicki swallowed, not realising she was taking great gulps of air. How could she hope to deny the obvious when not even the birthmark was to be disputed? She was aware of Wade, tall and lean, a bitter twist to his mouth, his broad shoulders, against which she had on too few occasions found comfort, cynically braced. There was not, on his expressionless face, one scrap of affection for either his wife or newly discovered son. His eyes were narrowed to dark, enigmatical slits, and as her own widened helplessly he turned away to walk to the window, evidently finding the view more interesting than his wife.

Feeling sick again, Vicki realised he would never forgive her. If he was here today it could only be because his grandfather had left him with little alternative. Then she remembered Wade had never done anything unless he wanted to. Hope stirred in her heart, a confused hope but hope none the less. Could it be that Wade had actually come to stop his grandfather from taking Graham?

'How did you find us?' Not yet having the courage to put this theory into words, her mind veered drunkenly in another direction. As she spoke to the old man, who had at least always been brutally frank with her, her hands went out automatically to soothe the restless baby. Beneath her loving if distracted administrations, young Graham turned completely over, smiling in his sleep. Vicki's heart jerked. She knew that smile so well. As the old man had just pointed out, it was a living replica of Wade's. Wade's—in one of his rare, more gentle moments.

'How did we find you?' the old man snapped, without once taking his eyes from the cot. 'We found you because every thief makes a mistake sooner or later, my dear! Mind you, if I'd had any suspicion of this, I would have been after you as soon as you left. As things were, I didn't even know you and Wade were sleeping together. I had no proof that his marriage was anything but a desire to revenge himself on me. I had no idea you were expecting his child!'

As Vicki swayed dizzily, he went on, taking no notice of her chalky face, 'You went, madam, to the Royal Melbourne Show last month. A friend of mine told us he had seen you there with a boy, obviously your son, who could only be a McLeod. It's taken a little time to trace you. None of us suspected you would be living in such a hovel, or it might have been sooner.'

'I see.' Vicki's sapphire eyes were blank, and she met his contemptuous stare despairingly. It was true she had taken Graham to the show at Ascot Vale. He was almost four years old and, aware of his growing love for animals, she hadn't been able to resist it. The Melbourne Show being such a huge affair, she had convinced herself she would never be recognised. Wade, she had recalled, usually went to the Royal Sydney Show at Easter, which was even more enormous.

Graham, for all he was so young, had become obsessed with the livestock, the ring events and sideshows. Vicki, marvelling at his obviously inherited instincts for such things, had given in to his pleas and stayed longer than she had intended. Someone must have spotted her and told the McLeods. The world, she decided bitterly, was full of people who ought to know better!

Wade's silence appeared to encourage the old man—not that he ever needed any prompting to express exactly what was on his mind. 'I think you had a nerve, girl, to try and rear a McLeod in a room like this.'

Vicki's gaze wandered slowly about her. The room wasn't usually in such a clutter, but Graham was a growing boy who didn't yet know the meaning of tidiness, and she had felt too ill lately to restrain him much. It would never do to say so, however. These men, she could see, would use every weapon they could find to take Graham from her. How could she, with scarcely a penny to her name, hope to fight them alone? Unless Wade would help her.

Hope flared as she stared at her husband, as if willing him to turn and look at her. Graham was Wade's son. Without his consent the old man might have little say in the matter.

'Wade,' she begged, to his taut back, thinking to give him the loophole he might be seeking, 'you never wanted a son, you said so. And you don't really have definite proof.'

Before he could answer his grandfather exclaimed triumphantly, waving a paper which he took from his pocket. 'I have here a copy of the boy's birth certificate— Graham Wade McLeod! So we don't want to hear any more about him not being Wade's child. I regret he doesn't have a different mother, but once on the station he'll soon forget you. Any soft ways you've taught him can soon be stamped out.'

Fear caught Vicki by the throat, a horrible, all-consuming fear, such as she had felt only once or twice before. The first time had been on hearing her parents had been killed. The second, when Wade had sent her away, and the last time when she had been quite alone when Graham was born. But none of it had seemed worse than this. The old man's threats were like barbed shafts and she knew he meant every one of them. Wastage of speech had never been a McLeod failing. It wasn't so much concern for herself—long ago she had got past caring—it was what they would do to Graham. Soon they would have him as ruthless and arrogant as themselves.

'You—you can't take him from me! The law wouldn't allow you,' she cried hysterically, but her anguished gasp went unheard.

'The law, huh!' old man McLeod mocked. 'The law, girl, would take one look at this room—and you, and would come to the only possible decision. You don't stand a chance!'

'Wade!' Again Vicki appealed to her silent husband. Why didn't he say something? She knew appearances were against her, the conditions under which she was living. Even her illness. Her hair hung lank. The soft, pale gold, which Wade had once told her reminded him of a baby's, was now an almost ugly brown with nearly two weeks' neglect, and her usually clear skin was mottled and blotched with the fever she had. The robe she wore was mended and old because all her spare cash went towards Graham. Her body, under the robe, was thin, almost to emaciation, through her not having been able to eat for days. With a sinking heart Vicki realised she must be looking at least ten years older than barely twenty-three.

'I do have a job,' she said fiercely, to the old man, when Wade, instead of coming to her rescue, merely turned to stare at her indifferently, his dark eyes almost black. 'I know,' she continued, her soft mouth setting bravely, 'it could never compare with the McLeod empire, all those hundreds of thousands—or is it millions of acres—the stations you own, but it is a job!'

The old man laughed harshly. 'Do you expect young Gray to thank you for such an inheritance, for depriving him of his rightful one?'

'I call him Graham,' Vicki corrected dully. Senselessly she went on defying him, knowing she could never fully explain. She had wanted to call him Wade. The first time she had seen her son she had been determined to christen him by his father's name. This was until she had realised

that every time she used it it would bring terrible pain. So
it had had to be Graham, Wade's second name, one which
she believed his mother had declined to use. The old man,
Vicki knew, when he was addressed in any other way
nowadays, was always Gray, a shorter version of Graham.

'He's young enough yet,' old man McLeod was saying
smugly, 'to take kindly to change. And believe me,' his
tone changed menacingly, as he lowered his beetling brows
at the swaying girl before him, 'there's going to be some.'

Vicki's eyes widened on her tormentor, the pupils dilat-
ing with visible fear. Then, to her horror, the room began
reeling around her again. Whatever happened she must
get rid of them before she fainted. 'If you don't leave at
once,' she gasped, 'I'll call someone to throw you out!'

The old man snorted abusively. 'Now who do you
imagine is going to do that? Come on, Wade, we might as
well take the boy now and go.'

'No—you can't!' Vicki protested, shocked beyond everything, terrified! She was unable to believe such a thing
could actually be happening. Horror-stricken, she watched,
with a kind of frozen immobility, as he reached down with
his brown old hands to grasp the sleeping boy. It was then
that she flew at him, but even as she moved great waves
of darkness began hitting her and she knew no more. Her
last thought was that Wade had done nothing to help her.


When Vicki came around she found herself in bed. It was
a soft bed, it felt nice, and she only wanted to lie there. It
took real effort to raise her heavy eyelids properly, to force
her dazed eyes to wander round the room she lay in. She
realised she was in hospital. The white walls, the clinical
cleanliness left her in no doubt, and a fretful frown marred
the smooth paleness of her wide brow. It deepened in bewilderment as she discovered Wade by her bedside.

For the space of seconds her mind played her tricks. She
imagined she was back at Baccaroo, in another world. Wade
had been out all night, busy with the mustering on the

huge cattle station. His big body hadn't been there to keep her warm, but she could have sworn he had just kissed her. Her mouth, which he had taught to be so sensitive, felt as if it had been gently assaulted. 'Wade?' she whispered.

He was watching her, but his eyes were unreadable. If anything, there was just a hint of his well remembered caution. 'Yes?' was all he said.

Her frown deepening, she stared at him. Was this all he had to say? She couldn't recall him ever being inarticulate. Then, as she stared at him, everything came flooding back with terrifying force. Her voice rose in panic. 'Where's Graham? Wade, what have you done with him? Where am I?'

Because he took his time in answering she could have killed him, but when she tried to so much as sit up she was so weak she couldn't. The white walls around her appeared to mock the urgent appeal in her hands and face. The man she was looking at might have been a stranger, not someone who had once held her so closely.

'You're in hospital,' he told her briefly, easing his powerful limbs somewhat warily on the frail chair beneath him, 'and Grandfather has taken Graham home to Baccaroo.'

'No. Oh, no!' As full realisation hit her, Vicki's voice rose to a scream.

His hand moved like lightning, clamping ruthlessly over her mouth, his fingers biting the soft skin of her cheeks. 'Be quiet, you little fool! Unless you want me thrown out?'

She obeyed, although she didn't believe anyone could throw a McLeod out of anywhere, unless he chose to go voluntarily. That the touch of his hand made her face burn seemed of secondary importance. 'Wade,' she begged frantically, all her pride sliding from her, 'you can't take him from me!'

'I didn't.' As her voice modulated, he relaxed the guard of his hand. 'It was the old man's idea. I don't want him.'

Strange how that still hurt as much, Wade's rejection of what was actually a part of him. Even though she was familiar with McLeod history and knew the root cause of this, she was still surprised. 'I know you don't want him, you never did,' she forced herself to try and speak calmly, 'so why didn't you speak out? You could have prevented your grandfather coming, from taking him away!'

'The old man has a heart condition.'

'So?' Her voice dropped to a strangled whisper as her brief strength was sorely tried. 'I don't recall you ever worrying about him before. You hated him—for what he'd done to your family.'

Wade McLeod's face closed up. So near that she could see every sculptured bone of it, Vicki felt her whole body vibrate with remembered trembling. Odd, the insane recollections, when other, much more important things were at stake.

Curtly, Wade said, 'There's a difference, I've discovered, between hating someone and actually pushing them into their grave.' He paused, seeming to choose his words carefully. 'If he hadn't been there when I learnt of your whereabouts, I might have been able to arrange things differently. As he is now the least setback could kill him.'

'This worries you?'

Ignoring her cold sarcasm, he startled her, somewhat, by sighing heavily. 'It doesn't seem to matter so much now. If the sight of his great-grandson is going to add pleasure to the last few weeks of his life, who am I to begrudge him? It won't change anything much. There are other things he'll still go on about.'

'But I want my son!' In spite of her efforts, Vicki's voice rose again and she struggled to sit up. 'You can't take him from me, no matter how you feel about me!' Wildly she sought some outlet for the terrible despair inside her. 'I hate you for the past, Wade McLeod. Don't make me hate you for the future!'

'Don't worry,' she heard his breath rasp and his eyes went icy, 'you can have your son just as soon as the old man goes.'

'You've never forgiven me, have you,' she cried, 'in all this time?'

'We won't talk about it,' he cut in curtly.

'I thought you would have tried to divorce me,' she choked, hurt to the core, for both herself and Graham.

'After the old man goes,' Wade taunted, 'I'm going to see to a lot of things I've been putting off. Right now it gives me more pleasure, every time a classy new specimen of femininity puts in an appearance, to see him biting his fingers because there's no way I can marry the lady.'

'So you still use me like a weapon?' The hurt was building up now, becoming a floodtide, sweeping away the deep frozen inertia of the past four years. But, like cold fingers held too near the heat, the thawing was so painful she almost screamed. 'You never loved me, I know. You married me on a surge of anger. Because I was the last girl your grandfather would have chosen for you, and you decided to have your revenge by presenting him with your loveless childless marriage. As I said, you only wanted me as a weapon.' Vicki paused, suddenly frightened by the look on his face that she had said too much. Even so, Wade's answer, at that moment, seemed strangely more important than her fear.

Far from denying anything, as she had unconsciously hoped he would, he merely sneered, 'You were a good weapon, while it lasted, but like all weapons I should have remembered to use you carefully. Unfortunately I wasn't careful enough.'

'Well, you can't use me now,' she was unaware of the painful disappointment in her eyes, 'because I'm not at Baccaroo any more. I'm going back, but only to collect Graham.'

'No, you aren't.' His hand shot out to cover hers, his grip menacing with anger. 'You're going back to Baccaroo to stay—for as long as the old man lives. After that you'll be free to go, both you and your son.'

While Vicki wanted to argue, to deride him for his cruel

rejection of her, his ruthless attitude swept every logical argument from her mind. She could only stare at him, entirely and helplessly wounded. She wanted to pursue the matter, to make him understand he must try and see her point of view, but knowing of his harshness in the past she took heed of some instinct which warned her to go carefully.

Not wholly aware of doing it, she avoided any direct reference to his last observation. Her face was white, but she managed to ask evenly, 'I'm in hospital, aren't I? How did I get here?'

'I brought you. You've been here three days.'

'Three days!' Wade had released her hand. Now she clutched his, her face tormented, her voice rising. How was Graham managing without her? 'Have I been so ill?'

'You had a virus fever which went untreated too long, but you should be all right. You haven't been unconscious all the time. Partly you're suffering from exhaustion.'

'And Graham?' Her eyes begged what she couldn't put into words.

'Stop worrying about him,' Wade exclaimed grimly, his mouth so hard with a kind of leashed fury that she couldn't bear looking at him. 'The old man hired a nurse. God knows she should be efficient, she's costing plenty. They flew out of here a few hours after you passed out.'

'But he's only been used to me!'

'Come off it, Vicki, you had a job.'

'Yes. Oh, I see,' she faltered unevenly. Then, seeking to assure him that Graham hadn't been neglected through her having to work, she said, 'He is used to other people, but this is because I had no choice. The lady in the room across the landing looked after him. She's very kind, he has much of his own way.'

'Then a little discipline will do him no harm.' For a man who never had anything to do with children he sounded remarkably well informed. There were, of course, children on the station. 'Anyway,' Wade shrugged carelessly, 'it appears he's settling fine—more pleased with everything than his mother ever was.'

As if Wade had struck her she removed her hand from where it still clutched his and pushed it under the bed-clothes. She had loved Baccaroo, but if he thought other-wise then let him. Graham, she knew desolately, would love it too. There would be so much at Baccaroo to take his attention. All those horses, for instance. The station ran some of the finest in the Territory. Graham would be delighted with them, young though he was. How long would it take a boy of his age to forget previous attachments when confronted with all Baccaroo could offer? But she couldn't agree to this without a fight.

'I refuse to leave him there!'

The movement of her hand brought a grim smile and, as if in retaliation, Wade took no notice of her increasing agitation. 'Your hair,' he touched it fleetingly, 'it never used to be so dark? The old man used to say its fairness couldn't be natural. Was he right?'

While resenting the ease with which he sought to change the subject, she couldn't help protesting, 'I had no hair-dresser, no magic means of making my hair lighter than it naturally was at Baccaroo.' She wasn't interested in her hair or anything else about herself. She couldn't find the energy to tell him her hair was only suffering from neglect, that all it needed was a good wash. To recall the few times Wade had run his hands over it, on days when it had looked as silky and fluffy as thistledown, brought pain, so she tried to think of something else.

She wished he would stop looking at her. He had always had a most penetrating gaze, his eyes often seeing far too much. He might be king of his many acres at Baccaroo, where he ruled, in spite of his grandfather, with all the autocracy of a more feudal era, but he didn't rule over her! This, bringing a positive surge of temper, gave her the strength to try and struggle up. When his hand came out to push her back against her pillows, as he had done a few minutes ago, she could have cried with frustration. Despair almost swamped her, that when his fingers touched her shoulders a flicker of awareness went immediately through her. Her eyes widened, giving a transient beauty to her ravaged face as she stared up at him. If only he hadn't been so attractive, so frighteningly masculine! There was about him a kind of sensuous hardness that made her want to turn over and curl up into the mattress. Dear God, that he could still affect her so after four long years! She must be raving—hadn't she enough to fight? Her illness must have deranged her.

If Wade McLeod was conscious of any desire other than to make his wife relax, he gave no indication. His hands didn't linger, but his eyes narrowed coldly on her face, as if some part of him remembered things against his better judgment. When he spoke his voice held merely a dry cynicism. 'I hope we'll soon be able to improve your looks at Baccaroo, even if you were always a plain little thing. At least I've made a start on your wardrobe.'

Colour swept up her cheeks, making the blotching worse, so she knew she must deserve the way he described her. It was no use flinching. 'My wardrobe?' Startled out of her painfully held composure, her eyes dropped to the flimsy nightgown she was wearing. It was, she thought, much too transparent. Perhaps it was as well she was so thin as it must leave little to the imagination! Had Wade chosen it himself? 'This isn't mine,' she stammered, attempting to pull the sheet higher, under her chin. 'Where did you get it?'

Sardonically, he leant back in his chair, hooking both arms around the sides of it. The broadness of his chest, thus bared, caused Vicki's face to burn anew with recollections and a pulse raced in her throat as she looked away.

'I suppose you just went out and bought it?' she said dully.

'Nothing a man need be ashamed of doing,' he said smoothly, 'if it's for his wife.'

She might have replied that he had never bought her such a thing before, but she remembered the special circumstances. What, she wondered, did he buy other women?

When she remained silent, his mouth twisted. 'If you must know, I tracked down your place of work.'

'You what!'

'I'm beginning to see,' his eyes appraised her coldly, 'it's going to be easier to tell you everything. You fainted right into my arms. The old man was shouting that you were a good actress and then your son woke up. Someone had to take charge.'

'As if you didn't, always!'

He ignored her bitterness so that she almost felt ashamed. 'I could see you were too far gone for the usual methods of resuscitation, even if there had been anything in that hovel to revive you, so I simply whipped you into hospital.'

'And Graham?' The tears in her voice were streaming down her cheeks now as she thought of his baby mind trying to grapple with such a rude awakening. Of seeing his mother taken from him by a stranger!

Wade had no compassion for tears. 'I contacted a neighbour—obviously the woman you were talking about.' His tone suggested he hadn't been impressed, but he did say grudgingly, 'She helped. Grandfather stayed with the boy until I returned, then we took him to a hotel. You can believe me he didn't bawl the place down. I'll say this for him, he has a stiffer upper lip than you have! The old man talked to him and he went off to sleep again. The next morning he wanted you, but not for long. He has too healthy an interest in his surroundings to fret overmuch.'

Vicki believed it, even while she felt stunned, as if from a blow. Graham had too much of the McLeods in him to allow himself to become overwhelmed by petty considerations, like losing his mother! Even at so young an age he had it in him to conduct himself like a man. His wouldn't be the normal reactions of an ordinary four-year-old. And from now on, if old man McLeod had anything to do with it, this tough, independent streak, which already flourished in him so abundantly, would be encouraged until soon he would be no baby any more.

'What then?' she breathed, trying desperately to control another wave of tears. She must be weak because of her illness.

Wade glanced at her oppressively, noting how she shivered. 'It didn't take long to organise the rest. A nurse from the agency, then I saw them all off from Moorabbin Airport.'

Not for a moment did Vicki doubt him. In the months she had lived with the McLeods she had become very aware of their superb efficiency. They had only to devise a plan to have it immediately carried out, especially when money was no object.

'You have plenty of power—and you enjoy using it!' she choked, attempting not to think of Graham, in case her last bit of restraint went.

'It helps.'

She could see he barely concealed his impatience with her distress. 'Why didn't you go with them?' she asked, feeling sick.

'I decided not to.' He gave no explanation, nor did his face betray anything. 'I went to your place of work in Collins Street and told them you wouldn't be back.'

'You—what?'

He regarded her wild resentment suavely. 'You can't be in two places at once.'

Helplessly she subsided. 'What did Madame Sorelle have to say when you told her that?'

'Nothing at all,' he assured her cynically. 'At least nothing you wouldn't want to hear. Considering the bill I paid perhaps it wasn't surprising.'

'Bill? For what?'

'For all the new clothes I bought you, that nightdress you're wearing included. It seemed sensible to get them there. In a high class establishment, where you'd worked. Madame Sorelle said you'd occasionally modelled for her, when one of her other girls was off, so she knew your size. You didn't think I was going to take you back to Baccaroo as you were, did you?'

Was it pride or concern that had made him do this? Somehow she imagined the first would be responsible. 'You could have packed me something from my room. My pyjamas ...'

'If I could have done, I'd have put a match to the lot of it! It would have given me the greatest pleasure to see it go up in flames.' His laughter, which followed her visible apprehension, had a grim but satisfied ring to it. 'As it happened, I was able to hire someone to clear everything out, and the room's been re-let. It would be impossible for you to go back there, even if you wanted to.'

## CHAPTER TWO

It seemed a long time before Vicki could pull herself together sufficiently to speak again. The room Wade referred to so contemptuously had been the only home she had known, since before Graham had been born. And in the space of a few hours, probably less, Wade had destroyed it. It only made everything worse to realise she couldn't fight him on this, not if she wanted to see Graham again. She wasn't fool enough to imagine she could take on Wade McLeod and win. There might be a way, but it would need patience to beat him at his own game. Not having to pretend the weakness which seemed suddenly to overtake her, she whispered thickly, 'Not everyone can afford to live on places like Baccaroo!'

He didn't have anything to say to what sounded suspiciously like an accusation, but his eyes narrowed on her taut face.

Suddenly she had to know. It was like a pain gnawing inside her. 'Wade, don't you feel anything for your son?' Every nerve tense, she waited for his answer.

He gave none, not directly, but came to his feet with the swiftness of movement she so well remembered. He saw how white she was, the unconscious pleading in her blue eyes. Eyes which begged an answer he wasn't prepared to give.

Unrelentingly he stood gazing down at her. 'You understand how I feel about him, my dear. We don't have to cover old ground, open old wounds. I'll pick you up on Thursday morning—your doctor assures me you should be well enough to travel by then. I should advise you to regard the next few weeks at Baccaroo as an unexpected holiday and learn to be content with that.'

When he strode out, Vicki considered it crazy to feel hurt that he never spared her another glance. It seemed even more insane, considering her very real anguish over her son, how it was Wade who held her every thought, at that moment, rather than Graham.

Four days later they flew north to Alice Springs, where they transferred to Wade's private plane which would take them to Baccaroo. The journey from Melbourne had been pleasant, another time Vicki might have enjoyed it, but she still felt horribly weak.

Wade turned his dark head to glance at her, not fooled by the huge sun-glasses which half hid her pale face. 'You've had about enough, haven't you?'

'You don't have to worry about me,' she replied coldly, looking straight ahead, rather than at the man sitting beside her, as if afraid to trust her eyes not to linger. He flew the plane with the same expertise he did everything else, which included, she recalled with a shudder, reading her very thoughts. She didn't know what she was thinking about—telling Wade not to worry about her! If he did that, it would only be for the sake of appearances.

He brushed aside her brief protest impatiently, his interest, as she suspected, impersonal. 'I'd have the same concern for anyone practically just out of a hospital bed. You have an altogether too fragile look about you. I wanted you to spend the night in Alice, remember?'

'Yes, I know,' she murmured evasively, 'but I must get back to Graham.' She didn't add this was only one of the reasons she had been reluctant to stay in Alice. Wade was a stranger, he had changed. While, she, in many respects, felt not much different from the vulnerable eighteen-year-old he had married. She had been frightened he might have asked her to share a bedroom, that he might have forced her to do so if she had refused.

Wade sighed, as if clamping down on some impatience. 'Graham's okay. I've checked.'

'So you've already told me,' she retorted fretfully. 'You

keep on saying everything is fine, but you'd take Graham away from me, if you could, with the same emotion you feel when you wean one of your thousands of poor calves!'

He turned to look at her again, his eyes glinting with anger. If he exercised a certain control, it obviously didn't come too easily. 'You'd better relax,' he rejoined coldly. 'I don't think this kind of talk's going to get you very far. You talk of wanting to keep your son, but if you don't let up you'll never be fit enough again to even look after yourself.'

Vicki threw him a sullen glance, tears stinging the backs of her eyes. Hadn't he always excelled when it came to dishing out advice! His imperious manner never allowed one to imagine he could ever be wrong. Unwillingly her eyes clung to the hard, handsome length of him, to the lean, well shaped hands on the controls. How well she remembered those same hands on her body, controlling and directing her young, feverish passion, so that her desire might ultimately reach the same heights as his.

Swallowing convulsively, she looked quickly away from his hands, back to his broad shoulders. He must be a lot cooler than she was, in his short-sleeved shirt. Quietly she slid out of the little blouson she wore. It was much hotter here than in Melbourne and the jacket felt heavy. She ignored Wade's frowning glance. There had been, or there seemed to have been, a flicker of renewed interest in it since he had met her that morning. She realised, when he had first seen her again, over a week ago, she had probably appeared even plainer than he remembered. Now, in the slim-fitting pants and brief top which Madame Sorelle had included in the clothes Wade had bought, Vicki knew he was faintly intrigued by the difference. Rather nervously she wondered what he would think of her hair. Eventually, at the hospital, they had washed it for her, restoring it to its former glory. Then, for no clear reason she could think of, she had asked a nurse to purchase a silky scarf, with which to conceal it from Wade's eyes. It might seem illogical, but

she wanted to surprise him. All because she seemed to remember either Wade or his grandfather doubting it had
ever been fair at all!

Madame Sorelle, Vicki recalled, had always been delighted with it. No doubt she, too, would have been dis-
pleased, had she seen it during the time she had been ill.
After Graham had been born, and she had found work in
Madame Sorelle's office, she had, one day, sighed ruefully
about being plain.

Madame, with her sharp ears, had overheard and thrown
up her hands in protest. 'Plain?' she had cried. 'My dear
child, just put yourself in my hands and I will make you
quite lovely! Such good bones, *ma chère,* such wonderful
clean lines. Those eyes, that skin, your hair! Right now
you may look a little plain because you haven't learnt how
to make the most of yourself, but you could be remarkable,
*chérie,* with just a little effort.'

Vicki, feeling too drained to care much what happened
to her, had let Madame have her way, although she had
never thought herself to be as pretty as Madame was fond
of making out. Because she had been terrified of being
recognised, she had always refused to work in Madame's
salon. Only occasionally, when they had been short-staffed,
had she agreed to help out. It was then she had seen the
admiring glances of the husbands and brothers of Madame's
wealthy clientele, had received invitations from several men,
as well as promises of their serious intentions. All had been
turned down because of her love for a small boy. Or had it
also had something to do with Wade? Unhappily Vicki
stared at her husband, attempting to disregard her traitor-
ous pulse. It couldn't have been because she still loved him.
It had surely only been that she had wished for no complica-
tions which might adversely affect her custody of Graham
in the event of a divorce.

Wade, as if conscious of her despairing glance, met it.
He stared straight into her eyes, then appeared to study
her mouth. 'You're different,' he commented.

'I've always been on the thin side.' She wasn't sure, but she felt he must be speaking of her looks. 'You said so the first time you saw me.'

From the corner of her eye, as she glanced away, she saw his mouth tighten, as if there were some things he would rather forget. 'Sure, you were then,' he drawled, 'but not all over. At least you weren't when you left.'

Feeling her cheeks flush a dull red, Vicki closed her eyes. Let him think she slept. But, even when she couldn't see him, he still seemed able to torment her.

Pictures flashed across her unwilling mind, all bound up with the semi-arid land over which they were travelling. There was the first time she had set foot on Baccaroo, the events leading up to it.

Two years previous to that, at sixteen, she had emigrated from England with her parents. When she was seventeen both her parents had been lost, touring the desert-like country in Southern Australia. There had been a build-up of circumstances, but tragedy might have been averted if they had taken sensible precautions. As it was Vicki had been left an orphan, with no money behind her, her father having just begun to re-establish himself as an architect.

Vicki could type, but this was about all. When the agency had told her of a job going at Baccaroo, a cattle station in the Northern Territory, near the Barkly Tableland, she had taken it immediately. Hadn't it seemed to fit her exactly? A wealthy pastoral family wanted a companion of Vicki's age for a girl, a seventeen-year-old relation, for about three months. Some typing experience would be useful, they had stipulated, for dealing with various things connected with the domestic side of the station, which the general office considered a nuisance. They required someone well spoken, quiet—and plain. Only Vicki hadn't known of the last condition until after she had arrived.

A few days later she had been on her way, relieved to escape from Canberra, Australia's capital, where she and her parents had been so happy. In the kindest possible way people had advised her to return to England, but she had had no one to go to there. Not that she told anyone this. Imaginary relatives could be better than none at all. Not even to the McLeods, after she had arrived, had she confessed to being absolutely alone in the world. Besides, Australia had become her adopted country and already she was fond of it.

The Australia she had known in the two years or so she had lived there seemed to Vicki all sunshine and light, the people mostly lighthearted and happy, but she had found a different atmosphere at Baccaroo. Almost as soon as she stepped over the threshold of the plain but substantial house she had known something was wrong.

Wade's grandfather had been there to meet her, old Graham McLeod, known to everyone, she soon learnt, as the Old Man. He had been waiting to introduce her to the pretty young distant relation whose companion she was to be for one long vacation. Until her parents sent for her. They had welcomed her pleasantly, Old Man McLeod even approvingly. Vicki realised later this was because she looked very ordinary.

Wade, that day, had appeared briefly in the background, a tall, tight-lipped figure who had scarcely spared her a second glance. Even on that first occasion he had made her heart race with a curious awareness and she hadn't been too young to realise that, though he was grim, he was attractive. He was a man to make any woman wish she was beautiful, but his eyes had merely been mocking as he had turned away.

Vicki had bitten her lip, momentarily diverted from the Old Man's gruff mutterings. It was scarcely the time to become conscious of her own shortcomings, but she had been keenly resentful that Wade McLeod, with a single glance, had made her bitterly aware she was less than perfect. She was of medium height and thin, her eyes, her best feature, huge and still deeply shadowed with pain through the loss of her father and mother. Her hair, on the

advice of those familiar with the heat of the Territory, was
cut too short. This, and its soft fairness, had made her look
like a boy, a very young boy at that!

In spite of her doubts, Vicki had survived that first confrontation even if her initial bewilderment over Baccaroo
remained. It had been something in the atmosphere. The
house should have been pleasant, with its dull but spacious
rooms, the wide verandahs, through which it was possible
to walk on to lawns kept green by what methods she never
knew, but the feeling that something was wrong was one
she never got rid of. It wasn't until she had learnt a few
of Baccaroo's grim secrets that she began to understand.

'Asleep?'

The voice of her husband jerked her from her half
dreaming state, but she turned her head sharply, not wishing him to see she recalled other times he had asked the
same question. On one or two nights long ago. His voice
hadn't been curt, as it was now; it had been deep and intimate, almost as urgent as his breath against her warm
cheek.

'No!' With a little gasp she came upright. She scarcely
realised that her reply, this afternoon, was the same as it
had been then. Only then it had been laced with an in-
credibly eager yearning.

'Look down,' Wade commanded, and when she complied,
'do you see where you are now?'

The big jets flew so high that one part of the world
seemed very much like another, but from a smaller plane
it was easy to pick out individual details. She could see they
were passing over the Barkly Highway, which joined the
Stuart Highway north of Tennant Creek. Before them
stretched the Barkly Tableland where Wade and his grandfather owned some of their thousands of acres.

Nervously Vicki closed her eyes, never having expected
to be so overwhelmed by such a sense of homecoming. Since
she had left it she knew she could never honestly deny
there hadn't been a single day when she hadn't thought of

Baccaroo, but she had never been prepared for such an extravagant surge of delight. For all she felt only like tumbling into bed and resting her tired body for a hundred years, to gaze down on all that red, endless space was like coming alive again. She had lived here for something less than a year, yet she had come to love it. The wide, almost featureless plains, covered by acacia scrub and low eucalypt, the semi-desert grasses. The outback, the emptiness, the unbroken horizons, the wide, wide skies. The heat, the lack of water. It wasn't so much lack of water, she remembered, as lack of rain. The big bores coped with the former admirably, but they couldn't supply the rain which made the grass grow for stock. It was a hard life, so hard that only graziers like the McLeods survived. They might make their millions, but survival here was an endless struggle against the elements. Yet it had broken her heart to leave it, just over four years ago, when Wade had told her to get out and never come back.

'Yes,' she whispered, unaware, as she looked at him, that her eyes were full of tears, 'I know where we are now. We'll soon be home ...' She spoke the word slowly, her tongue curling around it softly, unconsciously revealing. Then she stiffened. 'But it won't be like Melbourne, where the people in hospital had no reason to suspect we were anything but a normal married couple. What do you intend telling everyone, Wade?'

His face hardened, and she knew she had been a fool to imagine he felt he had to account to anyone but himself. He was a grazier, part owner of what, to Vicki, seemed almost half the universe. A pastoralist who reared cattle on a huge holding was considered superior, the privileged squatocracy. It could only breed arrogance, and this Wade had in abundance—this she had learnt the hard way! That he had other traits, such as brains and brawn, a powerful ability to command and, at the same time, work with his men, Vicki chose to forget. When she had been eighteen she had looked on him as a kind of god and loved him with a kind of awestruck reverence. Now she wasn't sure what was where that love had been. There was still awareness, an almost painful sensation in her breast each time she looked at him, but not like anything she had known before. She was vaguely conscious of something different being born inside her, but nothing she could come to terms with yet.

What Wade said next didn't surprise her. 'We don't have to explain anything.'

Not at all convinced, Vicki frowned anxiously. 'But what about all the people on the station? You used to employ an awful lot.'

'So?'

'How do you mean—so?' she very nearly screamed at him, her nerves taut, the dignity of her additional years almost forgotten. 'I have to be considered now, haven't I? I'm not a young girl any more, to be used for your own convenience and treated as though I didn't matter!'

'If I recall,' he jeered, 'you didn't object much to the way I used to treat you. You might still have been here yet, quite content with your lot, but for your own stupidity.'

A knife went through her, cutting and searing until she could have writhed with pain. Her face went white and strained and though she made herself speak she felt more like moaning. 'You had to bring that up, I suppose, but that wasn't what I was talking about.'

'No,' he agreed, his tone resuming normal, his eyes straight ahead, 'but you could try making yourself clear.'

'I know it may sound silly, but I feel slightly nervous,' she faltered.

'Four years ago you were nervous all the time. Now you surprise me.'

'Why?'

'I'm not sure yet,' his voice was no harder than his slanting glance and just about as forgiving. 'I told you I thought you'd changed. What I have to discover is whether you've done it yourself or with the aid of some man. Maybe more than one?'

'Wade McLeod,' said Vicki, very coolly and levelly— she was feeling far from both but pressed back on her scalding anger. 'Mr McLeod,' she repeated foolishly, 'if you weren't flying this plane I'd try to hit you!'

This threat he disregarded with devilish irony. 'You were learning fast when you left me. Don't ask me to believe you've had all that tender young passion on ice for four years!'

'You can believe what the—what you like!' she burst out, clenching her hands into balls of fury. The hurt reappeared, that he could remind her. 'I refuse to continue such a degrading conversation. As far as passion goes I don't want anything more to do with it, but whatever I do in future, Wade McLeod, it's my own business.'

'Not while you're still using my name.' His mouth set like a clamp, he stared at her.

'I can do that,' she took a bracing breath, 'even after we're divorced.'

'We aren't, yet.'

'So I must take warning?' Bitterly she wondered where all the pleasure of her homecoming had gone. She felt ill again—overcome by weakness. Knowing her own limitations when it came to sparring with Wade, she breathed deeply. 'Just tell me,' she pleaded, 'what I have to say to people about my absence?'

'Nothing,' he replied curtly. 'It's not exactly news, after all. They've probably given up conjecturing long ago. I assure you no one will tackle you about it, not unless you continue to call me Mr McLeod. That might really get them going again.'

'So there was talk when I left?'

'Nothing which wasn't easily dismissed.'

Vicki wondered how, her eyes darkening with bewilderment, a certain unhappy resignation, 'I expect you feel I ought to be grateful?'

'Well now, my little pommy,' he mocked, 'I was never aware that gratitude was one of your more admirable traits. From you I expect nothing. Most things in the past that I had from you I had to take.'

Drawing a ragged breath, she fought for control. She could comment on that, if she hadn't suspected he was deliberately provoking her. 'You make it difficult for a woman to express any appreciation.'

He sighed dryly. 'You talk of a woman as if you referred to yourself. If so you must have changed. You were never responsible enough.'

'Maybe I have,' she muttered bleakly, knowing instinctively that he was reminding her cruelly of the morning he had discovered she was expecting Graham. Among other things, he had thrown that at her. Was his mind still so warped, still engrossed with old hatreds? Her heart sank despondently. What might she not have to protect Graham from? It could be a blessing he was too young to understand such things.

When she fell silent he said, at last, tersely, 'Observe the priorities and leave the rest to me. You don't have to worry.'

They were approaching the station. Far away to the left she could see the homestead, the sheds, the stock pens, the staff quarters. Time seemed to push up against her, growing terribly short. 'Wade,' she asked, her voice suddenly urgent, 'has nothing changed between your grandfather and you?'

'No.'

Staring at his closed up face, she knew better than to pursue the matter further.

As if conscious of her apprehensive regard and wishing to build on it, he turned his dark gaze to her blue one. 'Don't you think you've pressed your luck far enough for one day?' he suggested grimly.

'Yes.' She wrenched her eyes from his and it took more effort than she cared to think about. She had wanted to discuss sleeping arrangements, that kind of thing, before they reached the house, but he was warning her that he wasn't prepared to listen. She must gather strength to approach him later. There were some things, he must realise, which couldn't be postponed indefinitely. One thing for sure—she would refuse to sleep within a hundred yards of him!

When they came down on the airstrip a utility was waiting, so she guessed Wade must have let them know when to expect him. Tears sprang to her eyes as she mutely allowed Wade to help her from the plane. It had been like that first time. Only then it had been Wade's overseer, Jeff Curry, who had brought her from Alice. On that day there had been none of the personal touch from the hierarchy, but she knew which hurt most.

Wade eyed the silk scarf still tied, gipsy-like, around her head, as if he felt a sudden necessity to keep to the mundane. 'There's a lot of dust, so perhaps it's just as well you have that thing on, although I'm beginning to wonder if you're thinking of sleeping in it.'

She blushed uncomfortably, sensing a taunt she didn't wholly understand.

'Don't panic,' he muttered sarcastically, while his interest centred speculatively on the tears she brushed quickly aside. 'No one's going to notice or care that your hair is a different colour, so you don't have to continue hiding it. So long as you have a proper hat for the sun?'

'If you tell me not to panic or worry once again, I'm going to scream!' she informed him, glaring fiercely up at him through her tears.

He laughed, the first time in a week she detected any real amusement. 'You seem to have a worse temper than I remember.' His finger went out to touch the dampness on her cheek. 'No need to let me drive you to tears of rage. I'm quite immune to women's tears, as you must know.'

She nodded. 'That and other things,' she rejoined angrily, jerking her head away as if his touch burnt her.

The stockman joined them before she could elaborate or
Wade reply. She had thought Wade would drive to the
house, but he didn't. He sat beside her, so close that her
body touched his, one strongly muscled arm along the back
of the seat, as if to prevent her from bruising. She wondered
if he had sat there deliberately to protect her from the
stockman's curious glances, which had been showered on
her in full measure when Wade had briefly introduced her
as his wife. Quickly she dismissed such an impression as
false. Whatever he intended she would rather have endured
the bumps and bruises than the churning hot feeling inside
her every time his arm tightened when she was thrown
against him.

At Baccaroo she couldn't wait to see Graham, picturing
a woebegone little boy trying hard to be brave, like herself.
The emotions which hit her were too mixed to be easily
decipherable when at last she found him. He was just back
from a riding lesson—too small to be learning to ride, she
thought anxiously, forgetting that Wade had ridden almost
before he could walk.

'Mummy!' Graham cried, showing a disquieting lack
of interest in Vicki's feverish hugging and kissing, her supposed to be comforting murmurings. 'I don't want to go
home. Grandpa says this is my home and I want to stay!'

The glance Vicki flashed at Wade was mutinous with
reproach, but she said nothing, just folded her arms more
firmly around Graham's small, squirming body.

See what you've done, her eyes said, but it didn't even
dent Wade's emotion-proof armour. He stood staring at
them, much as he had done when he had first seen them
together at the flat. She could tell nothing from his expression. Didn't he have an ounce of feeling?

Graham, wriggling from her arms, stared at Wade, his
eyes, the same colour as Wade's, round, but with curiosity
rather than fear. 'Are you my new father?'

Wade came to a sudden halt. He had taken a few strides
across the hall. He stopped abruptly. Vicki could see his

jaw set in a hard line, his face giving nothing away. 'You could say,' he replied laconically.

Graham tilted his chin, as if to see the tall man better, while he positively danced with excitement. 'I always knew I had one!' he piped shrilly. 'I told Mrs Parkes I had. Mummy once told me I was named for you. Can I call you Daddy?'

'You can call me Wade.'

Vicki's tears were now of anger. How could Wade be so heartless? She heard Graham repeating, 'Wade,' in a small, uncertain voice, as if he didn't much like it either.

Wade's eyes narrowed, but he didn't move, nor did he take his glance from the puzzled, less confident face upraised to his. 'Didn't you ever hear your mother use that name before?'

'No ...'

'Enlightening!'

'Graham darling,' Vicki could see he didn't understand Wade's last remark. His disappointment showed. 'It's probably better, darling, that you call this—this man Wade. We might not be staying long, you see.'

'But I want to!' She had certainly diverted him, if not in the way she had hoped. Beads of sweat broke out on her forehead. 'Grandpa says I can! He says——' Graham squared his small shoulders, his face taking on an authority which reminded Vicki devastatingly of Wade, 'Grampa says Baccroo will all be mine one day, so I must stay.'

'Baccaroo, darling,' she corrected him automatically, her clear English voice tinged with a bleak sadness that, already, Graham had every appearance of becoming one of *them*!

It was Wade who advised grimly, 'I shouldn't be counting your chicks before they hatch, young fellow.'

Again Graham didn't understand. 'What does that mean?' he asked intently.

'You'd better ask Mummy,' Wade drawled sarcastically. Then, instead of turning away, as Vicki expected him to do, he enquired harshly, 'Where's this nurse of yours, boy? Why isn't she here?'

'She's talking to Grandpa.'

'Is she now? Well, we'll soon see about that!' Wade strode over to the main sitting room door. In two seconds the nurse appeared, followed at a more leisurely pace by old Mr McLeod.

Vicki felt no surprise, being very familiar with the ease with which Wade got things done. She stared numbly at the efficiently starched nurse—nanny, she would be called in England. She remembered her father once mentioning that his mother had had one, but she had had no personal experience of such superior creatures herself. This one seemed brisk enough to cope with Graham's tantrums. She looked around thirty, and very attractive.

'Take your charge elsewhere,' Wade commanded, as if his son was of little consequence. 'I suggest bed!'

Graham, as if his father's lack of interest was at last getting through to him, reverted to being only four. 'Not going with her,' he muttered rudely, his bottom lip wobbling. 'I want Mummy!'

'You'll take what's good for you,' Wade replied brusquely, firmly removing Graham's arms from around Vicki's legs before they could begin to cling. 'Your mother is tired.'

'No, I'm not, Wade.' Vicki found her voice but could scarcely control its trembling. Need he act with such a heavy hand? It wasn't as if he wanted to have anything to do with the child! 'You forget,' she whispered, 'I haven't seen Graham in days.'

Wade, busy placing Graham imperviously with his nanny, took no notice. Surprisingly, Graham stopped protesting. Vicki felt indescribably hurt that he didn't continue fighting. From experience she knew him quite capable of doing so, when he wanted something badly enough. Apparently he didn't want his mother all that much!

'You'll be seeing plenty of him,' Wade countered briefly, turning back to her. He introduced her to the nanny, once he had Graham safely in her arms. 'I'm sure you'll soon get into Miss Webb's routine while she's here.'

There was nothing for it but to shake Miss Webb's awkwardly proffered hand, to return the cool smile and murmur something, politely. Mrs Parkes had often had charge of Graham, but with her Vicki had never felt this nervous apprehension. With the set-up here, old Mr McLeod and an efficient nurse, not to mention Wade himself, she could soon become unnecessary. Her heart shook, her throat went dry, and it didn't take the Old Man's clearly hostile stare to make her shiver!

Miss Webb whisked Graham off to bed, a task Vicki had never missed performing herself until this last week. As they disappeared she felt herself swaying . . .

Wade, beginning again to speak to her, caught her in time. Whipping her up in his arms, he cast one glance at her stark white face before starting across the hall. Over his shoulder he said tersely to his grandfather, 'She's still fairly weak and it's been a long day. I'll take her upstairs. You can send one of the girls.'

The hall righted itself before he had taken many more strides. Vicki protested, hot with embarrassment, 'Please put me down, Wade, I'll be all right.'

His arms merely tightened and he muttered diabolically, 'Shut up!' His tone was harsh, denying any real concern.

Limply she subsided against the hardness of his chest. Momentarily she was almost ready to admit defeat. She had thought she was better, but she only felt exhausted. The exhaustion was odd, not very reassuring. Other feelings began hitting her, too, as she was borne swiftly along in Wade's strong arms. She became conscious of his lithe easy stride, as if she was no weight at all. There was the warmth of his body which for so long she had been unable to forget. Beneath her cheek, in her ear, his heart beat heavily. She was conscious of the strength and masculinity of him, of his sureness. As seemed too often to be happening lately, Graham slipped from her mind.

Her conscience reminded her abruptly. 'I must be near Graham,' she said. 'Especially at night.'

'Is that another way of saying tactfully you don't want to be near me?' Wade asked frostily.

'No— I mean yes, in a way,' she stammered against his broad chest, which she felt heave with impatience. Never for a moment had she imagined Wade would want her beside him, even if she had been willing. 'Graham's used to having me near him, you see,' she added desperately. 'He's always slept in his cot beside me. I'll admit because we could never afford more than one room,' she finished unhappily, knowing she was making a poor job of presenting her side of things.

'A lot of things are going to be different now,' he said coldly. 'You must accept this. Graham has his own quarters along the corridor, which I'm sure you'll find he likes. Nurse Webb is next door.'

'How can you know all this?' Vicki asked resentfully. 'We've only just got back.'

'I sent instructions. I have no reason to suppose they weren't carried out.'

As if considering the argument closed, Wade quickened his footsteps. He thrust open a door, stalking through it, closing it again behind him. 'You will sleep here, in my dressing room. In novels it's always the unfortunate husband who does this, but I'm afraid I can't bring myself to be so charitable.'

Vicki felt too agitated to even glance at the room. Her eyes remained fixed on Wade's face as he lowered her abruptly into a chair. She scarcely knew what to say next. Her mind was so muddled she fastened on the first thought to enter it. 'How do you expect to divorce me if I sleep in here?'

'You must be ignorant,' he drawled, 'if you think this is going to prevent a divorce. That will be quickly arranged, when the time is right. It's the present which concerns me.'

Vicki's whole body felt cold, her lips stiff. She might

have known he had everything in hand, just waiting for the right moment! 'I suppose I'm to be in here so the staff can presume we are reconciled?' she asked flatly. 'I thought you said you didn't care what they thought?'

'No. I said I wasn't prepared to give explanations. This arrangement will at least prevent them from reaching any definite conclusions and save me from exaggerated speculation.'

Staring at him, Vicki tried desperately to pull herself together, to stop from shaking. 'Would you promise not to use the communicating door?' she asked hoarsely, feeling such a feeble suggestion was almost all there was left to her.

'I might—think about it,' his lip curled sarcastically, 'I might even ask you to promise the same. At the same time I could remind you that you weren't always so knotted up with such virtuous inhibitions. Once, I recall, you almost begged me to satisfy your sensual appetites, after I'd mistakenly aroused them.'

A kind of frozen anger—and shame—hit Vicki hard. 'You're unspeakable!' she gasped. 'I asked for a simple promise ...'

'It won't be necessary,' he cut in with grim cynicism, surveying her wide, sparkling eyes with an indifference which, to Vicki, seemed to speak for itself. 'Only on rare occasions have I allowed my feelings to outweigh my better judgment. It won't happen again.'

Colour burnt her cold cheeks. 'I should know just how deeply you regret the occasions you refer to!'

'I'm not here to talk of the past,' he dismissed her reference curtly. 'That holds little pleasure for me.'

He couldn't have put it more plainly. Shivering, she watched as he stalked to the door.

'Dinner will be at the usual time,' he spoke without obvious rancour. 'If you feel like joining us, after you've had a rest, well and good. If not, I'll bring you something up.'

'Couldn't you send one of the girls, or Mrs Clover?'

'Mrs Clover isn't here.'

'Not here?' Vicki wanted to get rid of Wade quickly, but this didn't stop her exclamation of dismay. Mrs Clover had been housekeeper at Baccaroo, and Vicki had reason to believe she had been her friend. She had been looking forward to seeing her. She had been counting on Mrs Clover's continuing support. 'Not here?' she repeated stupidly.

'There is such a thing as death.'

'Oh, I see.' Shocked by the news and remorseful, Vicki bit her lip. She wondered if she should commiserate further, then changed her mind. Emotions, apart from hate, had never seemed to play a great part in this house. She doubted if Mrs Clover, who had plodded her way steadily through a daily list of never-ending tasks, had ever been missed. Certainly no one might have genuinely mourned her.

'If you're really interested,' Wade McLeod mocked, 'you might like to know she was here until the end. Some women know the meaning of being faithful.'

# CHAPTER THREE

As the door closed behind Wade with deadly emphasis,
Vicki shuddered. So he still blamed her for what had happened? His arms, as he had carried her upstairs, had felt
oddly protective, but that must have been a cruel illusion.
He still hated her, as much as he apparently still hated his
grandfather and everything else.

She sighed, then suddenly her head lifted sharply as she
gazed around the room. She had been so agitated, so worried and absorbed about other things, she hadn't taken any
notice of her immediate surroundings. This was Wade's
dressing room, attached, with a bathroom in between, to
his bedroom. She scarcely remembered it. When they had
first married Wade had slept here. He had slept here almost all the time, apart from a few occasions during the
last few weeks of their somewhat stormy relationship. Vicki
had rarely come here; he hadn't allowed her.

Now she felt horrified and had to firmly restrain a desire
to rush hysterically after him, if her shaky limbs would have
allowed it. Surely he didn't expect her to spend six weeks
or so in a room like this? If he hadn't brought her here
himself she wouldn't have believed it! Numbly she nerved
herself to take another look around.

It was small and bare and might never have been occupied in the whole four years she had been away. Dust lay
abundantly everywhere, even on the cold lino under her
feet. The bed was narrow—no more, she felt sure, than a
small single, with iron rails. A mattress, about an inch thick,
reposed on it. There were a couple of old, threadbare
blankets, one grey-looking sheet and a lumpy pillow. The
whole room, as well as the bed, smelt musty and cold. It
seemed almost worse than the room she had left behind in

Melbourne. Why had Wade done this to her? Surely not even a strong desire for revenge could make a man act so cruelly?

About to go and furiously seek him out, she paused. She stood beside the door, breathing fast, her hands clenched, thinking. Shock still numbed her body, but her head felt surprisingly clear. Wade probably expected her to tear wildly after him, begging and pleading. And he wouldn't be anywhere she could find him. After being away for nearly two weeks, it would be unlikely anyhow if he would even be in the house. There was an adequate staff, but she knew from past experience that whenever he had been away he must personally check everything when he returned.

She was convinced, too, that no one would come near her. Old Mr McLeod would deliberately forget to send a girl up, as Wade, almost certainly, had known he would. Vicki guessed, that with all the fine rooms available, he wouldn't want anyone to see the one he had given his wife!

Her brow creased as she tried desperately to puzzle it all out. No one would believe that the wife of a McLeod, no matter what she had done, would be asked to sleep here. The girls employed in the house must know the room wasn't really fit for occupation. Consequently everyone must be assuming she was sharing Wade's bedroom—and bed!

Feeling bitterly angry and frustrated, Vicki ran a trembling hand over her forehead. As this seemed the only possible explanation she wondered, without finding any answer, why Wade should want to give this impression. Was it that he still wanted to annoy his grandfather? Surely he didn't imagine Miss Webb was going to make advances? Such attention from women had never rendered him helpless in the past, and there was no reason to suppose he had changed in this respect!

None of these conjectures ringing true, Vicki stumbled unhappily to the narrow bed and sat down. It seemed all beyond her. All she wanted to do was sink into a cool bed and sleep, and here she was, filled with such bewilderment that sleep would be impossible. She hated to confess, even to herself, how in hospital the thought of Baccaroo, its solid comfort, had somehow offset the humiliation of having to return.

Feeling the weight of self-pity bringing tears to her eyes, she shook her head impatiently and lifted her chin. Hadn't she been forced to rise above less than favourable circumstances in the past? There was no reason why she shouldn't do so again. After all, when old Mr McLeod died, she and Graham would again be out on their own. It was perhaps better that she didn't get too soft. If she could manage a good night's sleep she could do a lot with a mop and duster in the morning! And wouldn't she enjoy showing Wade McLeod that, though he might think himself a lord, he wasn't her master! Certainly she'd be a fool to let him think she was beaten yet!

Curiously strengthened, rather than defeated, by such a challenge, she rose and opened the door. Intuitively she had known she would find her suitcases there. Wade must have brought them up himself. Dragging them inside, she took out a bathrobe and cap and went into the bathroom. This, while austere, was more pleasantly appointed than her bedroom. There was no lock on the door, but she felt in no danger, knowing Wade wouldn't come in.

She ran water, sparkling hot, then turned on the cold tap before sliding out of her sticky clothes. She would bath, dress, then go downstairs and to hell with Wade McLeod and his grandfather!

An hour later, not feeling quite so brave, she forced herself to walk steadily to the dining room. She wasn't sure whether her strength was physical or came from anger, but she was sure she could make it. A small glow of triumph carried her on. She had managed to see Graham. He had been sleeping, but Miss Webb hadn't objected when she had pressed adoring little kisses on his small, contented face.

Not that she would have taken any notice if Miss Webb had, Vicki told herself firmly. All the same she had felt grateful there had been no occasion to assert her authority as his mother. She even felt a grudging liking for Miss Webb as she accompanied her downstairs, in spite of the fact that Miss Webb was asking far too many questions about Wade.

Vicki, not having expected to see Wade again that evening, felt herself stiffen on finding him in the dining room with his grandfather. The two men appeared to be discussing stock, which was about all they ever talked about, she remembered. Otherwise, apart from the general affairs of the station, they rarely had seemed to have anything much to say to each other. She noticed, with a despair which briefly confused her, that nothing had changed.

As she and Miss Webb entered the room, Wade rose to his feet. Old Mr McLeod did not. Vicki supposed it could be because of his health, but she wasn't convinced. She was aware that Wade's eyes hadn't left her, but she wasn't sure if it was appreciation she read in the glance which moved steadily over her. Perhaps it was her new dress that caught his attention. As he had bought it, and so recently, it could be no surprise, but maybe he hadn't realised how much it would improve her thin figure.

Vicki felt her cheeks go pink and she looked away from him. It was really puzzling that he had decided on such a dress, if he wanted to keep her entirely in the background. Of course he had taste, an astonishingly keen conception of how a woman should look, for all his fundamental contempt of them. Her dress was nice, in other circumstances she might have thanked him for it, but it was her hair which brought her the most satisfaction. When Wade had done with her body his eyes went to it and, for a brief moment, she caught a glimpse of startled admiration, as he noted the pale softness of it, of how it was longer than he had ever seen it. The boyish cut was gone. Now it hung loosely about her shoulders, giving her a delicate, arresting elegance she was barely aware of.

'Quite a transformation!' Wade grated, half under his breath, as he pushed in her chair. As he bent over her she could feel his breath, harsh on her cheek. A black, bewildering depression hit her. Obviously he wasn't as pleased as she'd thought!

Old Mr McLeod was staring at her, too, as if he didn't remember seeing her before. He spoke coldly, as her eyes met his defiantly over the table. 'I see you're well enough to walk downstairs by yourself.' Vicki knew he considered she hadn't really needed to be carried up them!

She forced herself to smile. 'I've had a good rest since then, Grandfather.' That should put him in his place! Never, during the weeks she had lived here as Wade's wife, had she ever dared—or been asked—to call the Old Man that! The intervening years must have changed her.

Wade was talking to Miss Webb and she didn't look at him. Much as she longed to let him see what she thought of him, because of her bedroom, she took pains to conceal her animosity. Whatever happened she mustn't give him the satisfaction of knowing how much this had initially upset her.

Yet it wasn't possible to keep her eyes from him altogether. As he spoke to Miss Webb, Vicki stole a glance at him and felt her heartbeats accelerate at his dark good looks. There could be no denying his attractiveness. He wore a shirt and tie but, unlike his grandfather, who was a stickler for such things, no jacket, and the strength and breadth of his shoulders almost kept her eyes riveted. No wonder Miss Webb appeared so entranced!

Wade's eyes, as if conscious of Vicki's wary stare, swung quickly to catch her in the act and the old magnetism which flared instantly between them caught her unawares. With a shudder of denial she looked swiftly away.

Throughout the meal old Mr McLeod scarcely spoke to

her again and, as she didn't feel much like speaking to Wade, Vicki addressed most of her remarks to Miss Webb. With a sense of relief she realised Miss Webb was an effusive talker, with the questionable knack of taking the conversation into her own hands. With someone like Wade she might not have succeeded in utterly dominating the dinner table, but tonight he seemed in no mind to raise any objections. She was disposed to give Vicki a graphic account of Graham's adventures, from the first hour of their arrival, whether Vicki wanted to hear or not.

'Graham loves it here, Mrs McLeod!' Miss Webb gazed at everyone enthusiastically, obviously wondering, Vicki thought wryly, why no one but old Mr McLeod gave any sign of pleasure. Wade grimly made no comment, while Vicki tried desperately to subdue the churning feeling inside her. Whatever happened she musn't allow Graham to become too fond of Baccaroo. She wondered just how much Miss Webb knew of the true situation. She must be a very perplexed woman if she only knew what Graham had told her. Listening rather nervously as Miss Webb chatted brightly on, Vicki felt the beginnings of a niggling headache. Was Miss Webb merely basing her remarks on what she had picked up from Graham, or was she fully aware that Wade McLeod hadn't been living with his wife and son?

She was even more disturbed when Miss Webb exclaimed to Wade, 'Your son is shaping extremely well in the saddle, Mr McLeod. He loves his pony and your stockmen are convinced he's a natural. He's had quite an audience these last few days. It does seem a shame he hasn't had an opportunity to learn to ride before now.'

The sudden silence which met her last remark seemed to go on for a long time. Wade spoke first, his eyes, as they flicked to his grandfather then back to Miss Webb, smouldering darkly. 'It appears you're interesting yourself in things which shouldn't concern you, Miss Webb. It's surely none of your business where he has lived. In future please concentrate on the job I pay you to do.'

'Oh, but,' not one bit perturbed, Miss Webb defended herself eagerly, 'a child's first years have to be taken into consideration, Mr McLeod. They often provide invaluable clues to their present conduct, to any regrettable characteristics they might have developed. Not that a boy of Graham's age could be held responsible, of course, but I'm afraid he does appear to be lacking in discipline and some of the more admirable traits.'

Recalling that these were almost Wade's very words, Vicki's cheeks scorched with humiliation. She waited, her heart beating over-loudly, to hear Wade's response to this. She herself was well aware that Graham wasn't particularly easy to manage. Maybe Miss Webb had felt it necessary to make clear that his wilfulness had been well-established before she took charge of him.

She wasn't sure whether to be angry or alarmed when Wade asked, with soft anger, 'Are you suggesting the child needs a psychiatrist, Miss Webb?'

It was old Mr McLeod who spoke first this time. He interrupted, pushing aside Wade's sarcastic suggestion impatiently. 'There's nothing wrong with young Graham that a month or two on Baccaroo won't put right. He's got more determination than most at his age, but then he's no ordinary young fellow. He's a McLeod through and through, in both looks and temperament, and it will take more than his mother and you to rule that out of him, Miss Webb.'

Miss Webb gave a little pout towards Wade and didn't reply. She seemed quite content to leave Graham alone, to concentrate on his father. Vicki saw the old man's eyes narrow suspiciously and felt suddenly sick. She decided not to wait for coffee. If it was anything like the rest of the meal she wouldn't be missing anything!

She rose from the table, with Wade's eyes on her. He seemed to have lost interest in Miss Webb. 'I think I'll go up, now, if you'll excuse me,' she addressed no one in particular.

'Of course,' Wade was polite but his voice was still edged with sarcasm. 'You haven't eaten much, but I hope you feel better. Shall I bring you some coffee?'

'No, thank you,' she choked, and escaped, forgetting to say goodnight to any of them. Surely Wade didn't intend playing the solicitous husband, after all he'd done and said!

'I won't be long,' he called after her. It was to Vicki the final outrage. What could he hope to gain by giving the impression that they were a normal husband and wife?

After looking in on Graham, who was still sleeping, she stumbled to her own room. An hour's absence hadn't improved it and her spirits sank even lower. The bed was bare, as cold as the room. She might easily freeze to death by the morning. There were only two blankets and she was forced to spread one over the dusty mattress and cover herself with the other. The sheet was in holes. She used it as an extra pillow.

Ten minutes later she was still cold. The nightwear she had found in her case was too thin to give the extra warmth she needed. She wished Madame Sorelle had included some warm pyjamas, but, like many people, Madame imagined the Northern Territory wilted under a perpetual heatwave. A lot of the time it did, but the nights could be extremely cold.

At last, unable to rest, Vicki gave way to temper. She would go to Wade's room and borrow some of his blankets. If she were quick he mightn't know they were gone. With a quiver she recalled that he had never worn much in bed, and sometimes when the bedclothes had slid to the floor he had never even noticed.

Unfortunately she wasn't quick enough. She was just helping herself to a thick rug when the door opened and in he came. Her throat went so dry she could only stare stupidly, although her apprehension must have showed.

'Why, hello!' he exclaimed softly, adding dryly, 'I didn't

expect to find you here—so soon.'

Taut with angry frustration, she looked up at him. Why hadn't she had the sense to come for the rug immediately she had come upstairs? He was narrowly looking down at her, just a hint of speculation in his eyes, and the weakness which suddenly invaded her limbs was not like that which she had known in her hospital bed. It made her back tingle and her toes curl into the thick carpet under her feet.

'You're trembling,' he said. 'I shouldn't have kept you waiting. I'll get you a drink.' His voice taunted.

The carpet reminded her somehow of the bare linoleum next door and brought a sane rush of impatience. 'I'm not waiting for you at all!' she cried, finding her tongue at last. 'I'm only here to borrow a blanket—I haven't enough and I don't want to bother the girls tonight.'

'I don't know about that.' He moved nearer, very near, and began removing his tie. As if fascinated she watched his long, lean fingers dealing with the knot. 'To hear you going on,' he quirked, 'I couldn't be blamed for thinking you were complaining about the accommodation I've provided. And you've only just arrived.'

The light drawl of his words didn't deceive her, not when there was steel behind the pretence of humour. It merely strengthened her conviction that he knew exactly what he was doing—which was more than she did, but it also made her all the more determined not to show any sense of injury. Her shrug was a masterpiece of indifference. 'It's easy enough to forget to check everything,' she said sweetly. 'I certainly wouldn't want to make a fuss over a blanket!'

Wade's tie came off and he began undoing buttons. Vicki tried to look away, tried not to feel mesmerised by the slow exposure of his broad chest covered by thick, dark hair. She mustn't remember what it had felt like against her own bare skin!

Frantically she wrenched her gaze from it, snatching the rug.

'Wait!' As his shirt came off, his hand caught her extended wrist. It might have been an accidental collision in mid-air, but she didn't think so. He said coldly, as if he had done with play-acting, 'You didn't come in here just to seek a blanket, did you?'

'Of course!' She felt unaccountably flustered, not enjoying the fiery sensations which seemed to flash from his hand through her body. 'I scarcely remember you using yours.'

'Not when I had you,' he mocked. 'You were warmer than any blanket.'

Her breathing fast, her eyes stormy, she wondered how he could be so despicable. How he could make remarks like that when his eyes on her face were totally without feeling. He had told her to go. Now he brought her back because of his grandfather, but had impressed on her very clearly that she was to leave again, just as soon as his grandfather died. Yet here he was, reminding her of her young, ill-advised passion, which for her had ended with his complete rejection!

'You're atrocious!' she choked. 'I hate you!'

His eyes hardened. 'Repeat that once more and I might give you something to really hate me for!'

'Oh!' she gasped, unable to manage more than that. Her face scarlet with suppressed feelings, she tugged at her wrist as his narrowed eyes watched her closely. When he looked at her like that she felt naked and was glad she wore her robe. If it had one fault it was too thin, the silky material revealed more than it concealed. She supposed she had Wade to thank for that!

He let go of her wrist but, to her dismay, slid his hand up her arm, to grasp the soft flesh above her elbow, drawing her to him. When she flinched, it might have been to punish her that his arms went completely around her, pulling her ruthlessly against him. Through the thinness of her robe she could feel the heat of his body, and molten fire poured through her veins. There seemed no stopping him and his effect was immediate and frightening. She tried to move, but again her trembling limbs prevented her, as his hands on her slim back pressed her against him.

'Wade—no. Let me go!' she made herself struggle, hit out at him.

His laughter was low, but it terrified her. He didn't do as she asked. There seemed only a desire to make her suffer as his hands laced tightly through her hair. He brought her head sharply against him, so she was crushed against the roughness of his chest, until her nostrils were filled with the male scent of him, forcing her to remember things she would rather forget. Beneath her shaking mouth his heart thundered so heavily she could hear it.

His voice was cool against the top of her head but oddly persuasive. 'You came to me, my dear. That must have taken courage. Why spoil it by pretending you're as innocent as when you left?'

Resentment flared through her, compounded of fright and pain, making her pulses race, her cheeks flame. She longed to slap those jeering words from his lips, yet the light which leapt to his eyes filled her with fear. 'You're despicable!' if she told him often enough he might believe it. 'I certainly didn't come in here tonight to take up where we left off. If you imagine I ever enjoyed sleeping with you then you're mistaken!'

'Liar!' his tone was wholly mocking. 'Or is it just that you need reminding?'

'Please, Wade!' She had meant to appeal to the better side of him but, as she raised wide blue eyes to his face and her full-lipped, enticing pink mouth trembled, she felt his whole body tense.

There was a sharp intake of his breath. Then the hand in her hair drew her head back and his mouth descended. His lips touched hers lightly at first, then hardened with increasing pressure, and, in spite of her horror of the situation, her lips parted under his. Response seemed to flood through her, overwhelming her with a half forgotten sensuality. His body was hard against hers, as a sudden violence seemed to take hold of him, and she felt his hands tearing savagely at the tightly closed front of her robe. In the process, as it opened, he touched her breasts and she wanted to scream and scream, as his hands burnt.

Amazingly, it was fear of the passionate surge of feeling within her that gave her the momentary strength to free herself. As he ruthlessly removed the robe from her shoulders, she jerked back so quickly she took him by surprise. 'How dare you do this to me?' she cried, shocked as much by her own reactions as by his reprehensible attitude. 'You brought me to Baccaroo to suit your own ends, not because I wanted to come,' she spluttered wildly. 'Don't think this gives you the right to do as you like with me!'

To her relief he made no attempt to recapture her again. He just stood staring at her, as if he had lost interest. He even viewed her attempts to pull her torn robe together without any change of expression. 'You little fool,' he snapped, his face as grim as ever she had seen it, 'go back to your own bed and keep away from me. I'm warning you, though, the next time you come in here deliberately to provoke me, I won't be answerable for the consequences. You remember what happened before? I'm sure you wouldn't be able to plead ignorance this time if it happened again!'

Vicki, already at the door, turned, her face ashen. 'I had to get a blanket. It wasn't my fault.'

'Are you referring to the blanket or the baby you had?' he asked coldly. 'As far as blankets go, why not have the lot?' He walked over to where she stood, thrusting a pile he had picked up into her arms. 'You'd better take them and get out, Mrs McLeod. I guess I won't need them. It will take me the rest of the night to cool down!'

He must have been talking of his temper, Vicki decided numbly as, an hour later, she still lay sleepless on her narrow bed. Bleakly she wondered about the other, how he could have said such dreadful things. The bed was warmer, now she had more to cover herself with, but in no way as nice as the one next door. With shame she found herself remembering the wide comfort of it, the wonder and delight she had eventually found there, in Wade's arms.

Suddenly she was back on the plane, her thoughts taking up where they had left off, when Wade had asked if she was asleep. She went back to the first day she had come here, on her eighteenth birthday. No one had known about that, of course. No one at all until Wade had asked.

Vicki remembered Alice Bell, whose companion she had been. Only a few months younger than Vicki, Alice had left after the vacation to join her parents in America. She was an only child, like Vicki, but unlike Vicki was used to a luxurious home and plenty of money. She had been inclined to criticise the Baccaroo homestead for its shabbiness, its lack of ultra-modern amenities, but other than that she and Vicki had got on admirably.

Vicki, strangely enough, had liked the house, both inside and out, from the very first moment she had seen it. The shabbiness, which she couldn't deny, had only made her feel more at home. It had been old Mr McLeod and his arrogant grandson whom she'd been nervous of, not the frayed curtains, the faded carpets and thin sheets. Sheets so worn that feet often went clean through them.

She hadn't been there long before she had found herself asking Mrs Clover, the housekeeper, if she couldn't mend some of the linen. Mrs Clover had agreed, with lazy good humour, that there was nothing to stop her trying —if she was crazy enough to want to do it.

The hand of a mistress being so clearly needed in the house, Vicki had somehow found courage to ask Mrs Clover about this, too, but the housekeeper had shaken her head. Mrs Clover had refused to be drawn, but Vicki had gathered the mysterious impression that there would never be a mistress at Baccaroo again. She had puzzled over it.

At first she had decided, with her young and innocent mind, that the lack of new linen and a mistress could be due to a shortage of money, that a lot of women would demand

at least an abundant supply of the latter before agreeing
to live on an isolated cattle station in the middle of nowhere.
Vaguely she had considered love, then dismissed it, knowing nothing then of its strength and power. She began to
view Wade McLeod's grim face with growing compassion,
before she realised it couldn't be money which prevented
him from taking a wife.

Usually after breakfast she had worked in the office for
an hour, as arranged, doing household accounts and writing
a few letters for old Mr McLeod. The old man didn't believe in spending more time in an office than was absolutely
essential, but slowly Vicki had learnt just how very ex-
tensive and varied the McLeod lands and interests were.
Her amazement and curiosity had grown. It certainly
couldn't be for financial reasons that Wade McLeod didn't
marry!

Nor physical ones, she was sure. She might have been
young, but she had become increasingly aware of his attractiveness, although, at almost thirty-three, he seemed far
beyond her in both age and experience. She spent a lot of
time wondering why he hadn't married. Women were
interested in him, she was left in little doubt. During the
first weeks of her stay at Baccaroo there had been several
extremely feminine visitors, invited, she believed, by old
Mr McLeod. Beautiful women, as she had every reason
to remember, as hadn't they referred to her as everything
from the maid to the office girl and general help? Usually
they had mentioned her as that quaint little thing with
eyes all over her face. Or the one with hair like short straw
and undeveloped figure. Well, it hadn't been undeveloped
by the time she had left, and many of those so refined ladies
had been laughing on the other side of their faces.

No matter—Vicki turned on her narrow bed, bitterly
unappreciative of her own sense of humour. After all, they
had had the last laugh!

It had been Wade's indifference to these women who
came and went that really aroused her curiosity. Oh, he

hadn't exactly ignored them. He had often appeared to encourage them. Once, when she had been going to the bathroom in the middle of the night, she had almost bumped into him leaving one of their bedrooms. A Miss Morris had occupied the room, a very lovely brunette. Vicki recalled Wade's face darkening with rage, as she had stared at him, open mouthed with horror.

'What's wrong, now, big eyes?' he had snapped. And, when she had remained silent but flushed a bright red, 'You should learn to keep your baby nose out of my affairs.'

'I—that's not true!' she had stuttered, meaning she had never poked it into them.

He had ignored this. 'I know you've been snooping around and I shouldn't like to see you hurt. Which happens to most people who don't mind their own business. How old are you?' he had asked abruptly.

'Eighteen.' She had found her voice, but not her equilibrium, thinking she must seem very naïve compared to Miss Morris.

Wade's eyes had flicked over her, the fine, clean lines of her, as if he was seeing her for the first time. His gaze had lingered. Mockingly he had drawled, 'All women seem to get amorous inclinations at this time of night, especially when they've nothing else to do but sit around all day. Are you asking to be kissed too?'

Vicki recalled thinking, with a sudden adult awareness, 'Not with the taste of her lips still on yours!' But before she had time to utter one word he had caught her to him, kissing her lightly, as if intent on administering only a brief punishment for the contempt he had so clearly seen in her eyes.

It was a kiss which might have stayed light if it hadn't been for the flash of instant awareness between them. Wade's whole body had become taut, like steel, as if there was something he didn't like, something which totally surprised him. Then, as if almost unconscious of doing so, he had gathered Vicki closer in his arms and crushed her lips beneath his. Even now she hadn't forgotten how the bruising pressure of his mouth had deepened, how for one insane moment she had clung to him.

The situation, for her, had been a new one, but not one she hadn't envisaged at some time or another in her natural girlish dreamings. It was the feeling which swept through her which she wasn't prepared for, the incredible devastation of her senses. She had been without the experience to prevent a revealing response. Scarcely aware of it, she had felt her body go amazingly soft in his arms. She had clung to him, fitting him like a glove, and the kiss had gone on and on.

When at last he had raised his head it had just been a fraction. Against her warm mouth he had muttered thickly, 'Come with me to my room, sweetheart.'

Vicki closed her eyes tightly now, remembering how painful it had been to tear herself away. She had had to remind herself sternly, through the clamouring chaos inside her, that she had never, would never, do such a thing.

As if the frightened stiffening of her slight body brought him to his senses, Wade had suddenly thrust her from him. His arms had slackened and he had let her go. 'God!' he said tightly, his face hardening with self-derision, 'I must be taking leave of my senses! Get back to bed, child.'

Still she hadn't been able to leave it alone. 'I'm not a child, Wade—Mr McLeod,' she had whispered dazedly, her eyes wide and appealing, begging, without knowing for what.

'You don't know what you're talking about, young Vicki,' he had returned grimly, occupying his lean hands with tightening the belt of his dressing gown. His face, as he had stared at her, had been devoid of any of the feelings she had sensed in him a few moments ago. 'No man wants to be accused of cradle-snatching. I might only be excused if it helps with your education. Or you can blame it on the lateness of the hour.' There had been sarcasm in his voice.

'Yes.' At last coming to her senses, she had taken one ashamed look at him and fled. Resolutely, back in her room, she had decided she must have been crazy. Yet it had kept her going hot and cold for days, the knowledge that had he asked her to go with him again, she might have been terribly tempted. It should have been comforting but somehow was not to find Wade ignored her even more than he had done before. The short episode, in the darkness of the night, might never have happened.

Eventually Vicki had persuaded herself to believe she had been disgusted by that brief encounter but, contrarily, it had made her curious to know more about the McLeods, their personal lives. This she soon discovered wasn't so easy. Trying to find out even about former McLeod wives was to come up against a blank wall. She didn't like to ask outsiders or visitors, but one night, when she was obviously disgruntled because old Mr McLeod had been particularly trying, Mrs Clover told her a little.

Wade was away, Alice up in her room writing letters. Vicki had been helping Mrs Clover wash up after the evening meal. It was the meal which old Mr McLeod had complained about and, for once, Vicki might have agreed with him, Mrs Clover being only an indifferent cook. She didn't think, though, it was quite as bad as he'd made out.

'Growls and grumbles!' Mrs Clover had snorted, shaken, for the first time Vicki could remember, from her perpetual good humour. Thumping down the crockery Vicki had dried so carefully, she had exclaimed, 'Sometimes I wonder why I stay! There are times when I can hardly work in such an atmosphere. It's been the same for years, Wade and his grandfather barely speaking to each other.'

Glancing at her, Vicki had held her breath, not daring to interrupt in case Mrs Clover stopped. She told herself she ought to have made some excuse and gone back to the drawing room, that she shouldn't be listening to something Mrs Clover might regret speaking of in the morning, but she had felt a sudden, urgent need to know why the two

McLeod men were such bad friends. Why a house with all
the makings of a wonderful family home seemed only to
hold a brooding, dismal silence.

When Mrs Clover had hesitated, as if trying not to allow
anger to get the better of discretion, Vicki had asked
quickly, 'Mr Wade appears to run the cattle stations. He
controls the business side of things, too, so why should he
treat his grandfather the way he does? He's polite enough
and all that, but it's almost as if old Mr McLeod was a
stranger.'

Mrs Clover had bristled, as Vicki found she always did
when the least criticism was levelled at Wade. This time
it had seemed to loosen her tongue as well, for she said,
'It's a long story, dear, and many people wouldn't believe
it. I couldn't begin to tell you the whole of it, but if Wade
doesn't treat the Old Man as kindly as he might, it's not
altogether to be wondered at! It really began when the
Old Man's parents unfortunately died in the desert country,
north of Alice. The Old Man was an only child and
Baccaroo became an obsession, as it still is, to him. He told
me himself that he swore to keep it in the McLeod name,
no matter what happened, and this was why he married
young : he was determined there should be future generations to carry on. It was a blow for him, as you can imagine,
Vicki, that he and his wife were denied the large family
they'd longed for and only had one son. That was Wade's
father.'

Mrs Clover had dropped her tea-towel at this point and
groped her way to the nearest chair. To Vicki it seemed the
housekeeper had almost forgotten she was there.

Staring into space, Mrs Clover had gone on, as if something was almost compelling her to talk of things she hadn't
mentioned for years. 'The Old Man gave his son no peace
until he married a girl he had chosen for him, but again a
McLeod union was blessed—some say cursed, with only
one child. Wade's mother died when he was thirteen and
there were no other children. None but Wade, Vicki, who

even then, before he went off to boarding school, was capable of doing a man's work. He also had several narrow escapes. Once he was nearly killed, which of course started the Old Man worrying again about the future. I was born on Baccaroo, dear, and always worked in the house, or I wouldn't have believed the way the Old Man used to go on!'

Breathlessly, Vicki asked, 'What sort of man was Wade's father?'

Mrs Clover sighed. 'He was a mild, easily led, man. Nothing like Wade or the Old Man. This was why, I suppose, he finally agreed to do as the Old Man wished. There was a young woman, you see, in Queensland, just over the border, and the Old Man ranted on about her until Wade's father promised he would go and ask the girl to marry him. The Old Man practically forced him, although Wade begged his father to stay at home. Wade was only young, but he would have had to be blind and deaf not to have known what was going on. I still remember, dear, as if it was yesterday. There was an awful row, but Wade's father went off and his plane, which he was flying himself, crashed and he was killed. Some thought he did it on purpose.'

'Oh, no!' Vicki felt her cheeks go white, and in her heart it was then that her dislike of Wade McLeod had begun to change. She seemed to picture him, no longer a child but not yet a man, his sorrow and anger. She had swallowed a lump in her throat and rubbed an unexpected tear from her eye. 'What happened then, Mrs Clover?' she had whispered.

Mrs Clover had stared at her blindly for a full minute before she had spoken again. 'Not a great deal,' she had said heavily. 'Wade simply swore to the Old Man that he'd never marry, that he would never supply any future generations. That's why Baccaroo is as it is today. The Old Man would do anything to make Wade consider marriage, but I'm afraid Wade never will.'

# CHAPTER FOUR

VICKI, pushing a long strand of fair hair from off her cheek, was surprised to find tears there. Were the tears because she would never see kind Mrs Clover again, or because she could still feel the emotion she had felt when Mrs Clover had told her some of the McLeod story? Perhaps it was a bit of both.

There were always aborigines on the station. They worked with the cattle, coming and going as their tribal customs dictated. Mrs Clover usually employed some of the girls in the house and might unconsciously have adopted some of their superstitions, for when Vicki married Wade Mrs Clover had declared she had somehow known it to be her duty to tell her about the McLeods. Only she hadn't told the whole of it. Vicki had been left to discover for herself the extent of the hatred and bitterness which seemed to have penetrated even the very walls of Baccaroo. And she had learnt the hard way.

Still unable to sleep, or to forget the way in which Wade had just kissed her, Vicki allowed her thoughts to go on. She recalled Mrs Clover's last words that evening.

'I don't think Wade will ever give in and I don't think his grandfather will ever give up, one being as stubborn as the other! The Old Man is always asking women here, daughters of old friends and the like, girls he approves of. He parades them in front of Wade and I'll not say they're unwilling! There's many a one who would give everything, even their virtue, if they thought it would help them become Wade McLeod's wife and mistress of Baccaroo. That Miss Morris was one of the first. I doubt if she'll be the last!'

Knowing the McLeod history had made a difference—at

least to Vicki it did. She had felt herself change after that. Where, before, she had sought to avoid Wade and his grandfather, she began to make a great effort to be extra pleasant. Often, as she had gone repeatedly over what Mrs Clover had told her, her heart had gone out to them. Although aware they wouldn't appreciate her sympathy she used to wish desperately that they could become completely reconciled. But that had been merely wishful thinking.

Strangely enough, she had felt sorriest for the Old Man, having come to like him, chiefly through working with him in the office. He was old, she'd realised, and too proud, but he did love Baccaroo. It was this love which, because she had been beginning to feel it herself, had seemed to excuse him a lot. In her eyes. She had thought him more to be pitied. It had seemed to her a terrible waste that Wade McLeod possessed such an unforgiving nature. It could only be crazy for a man to deprive himself of a wife and children just because of an old and senseless feud.

Leoda Morris had paid another visit and gone. So had Alice. Alice's parents had flown in to collect their daughter and stayed several days. They had been very grateful that Vicki had helped to make Alice's stay on the station so pleasant and had warmly invited her to visit them in America if ever she came there.

It was just after this that old Mr McLeod had asked Vicki to remain at Baccaroo. She had thought him a person who never acted on impulse, but she could have sworn he had done so then. She had been standing rather desolately in the garden when he had come across her, a young, lost-looking figure with her thin body and short straw-coloured hair. She had been staring out over the emptiness of the wide, red-coloured plains with such an expression of sadness in her arresting sapphire blue eyes.

Gruffly, as if catching himself doing something he didn't really approve of, the Old Man had halted beside her, asking what plans she had made for leaving. When Vicki had replied that she hadn't any but that she would be all right if someone took her as far as Alice, the Old Man had wondered if she would like to stay for a while. He had got used, he'd said, to having her around and found her useful.

For all she had imagined he would regret it in the morning, she had accepted eagerly. In those days she had grown to like him, and believed he had her. Had, until Wade had asked her to marry him. From then on the Old Man had shown her nothing but contempt.

Vicki's mind went back to that incredible evening when Wade had driven her out over the golden land, still drenched in hot sunshine, and stopped within the shade of a huge granite boulder and proposed to her. Then, because this was too painful to remember, she shied away from it and, quite suddenly fell asleep.

Sunshine was streaming through her bedroom window when she woke, although she saw it was not yet seven o'clock. Flinging back the tumble of blankets about her, she stumbled over the floor, not pleased to find herself still a little dizzy when she tried to move quickly.

She felt better when she reached the window. The Outback had always had this effect on her. When she had lived here, as soon as daylight appeared she had had to be up. Sometimes she had gone back to bed, but not often. Usually she had been out and about at dawn. It had become a habit, those early morning explorations, sometimes on foot, more often on the young filly Wade had given her, when she had seemed to have the world to herself. The only times she had missed was when she had wakened to find Wade in her bed—and that hadn't been often.

This morning she gazed with eyes which seemed almost greedy to make up for the years they had lost. The magic of dawn was everywhere, the sun's rays, pushing westwards, bringing an almost indescribable quality of beauty and light. It was dreamlike, the shades of shadow drifting black and white against a beautiful and hazy background of distant horizons. The birds were chirruping in the mulga and hakia trees and there was a wonderful scent of blossom from the garden. A few wisps of cloud patterned the sky, which on rare occasions meant rain, especially if the wind came from the west, but there was nothing about the dry, baked earth, this morning to suggest that any had fallen.

Soon, Vicki knew, the clouds would disappear as the sun rose higher, bringing stark reality to the heat soaked land. Temperatures would rise steadily throughout the day, for they were approaching the Australian summer. Not that she had ever found much difference in the seasons. September and October here were usually warm and windy with November and December the hottest months. The heat, in these parts anyway, was usually dry. This dry heat Vicki had never found tiring. If they did get a wet season it was between December and March, and this, she believed, with increased humidity, could be distinctly unpleasant.

With a sigh she turned from the window to face another day. There was too much to see to, to stand here dreaming. Quickly she found some jeans in her still unpacked suitcase, but frowned on them doubtfully. She wanted to take Graham out, to show him things she had discovered for herself before he was born. Things which had continued to enchant her all the time she had been at Baccaroo. In her growing excitement she had forgotten she must find the Old Man. Wade would be out with his men and she must make the most of the opportunity to try and find out if old Mr McLeod was really ill, that this wasn't just a story he had told Wade. Not that the old devil would be likely to confess to her, but she was intuitive. If she persevered she might get an inkling—if he was hiding the truth? If the Old Man really was ill then she would have to think again about taking Graham away. But first she must be convinced. In hospital she had had nothing to go on, apart from what Wade told her.

At last, deciding a cotton dress might be better for the house, and such a confrontation, she slipped into one, after showering. First, though, there was Graham. Running a comb through her shining hair, she went to find him.

Graham wasn't in his room, so she knocked on Miss Webb's door. She found Miss Webb still in bed, but there was no sign of Graham there either.

'I expect he'll be downstairs,' Miss Webb mumbled, emerging sleepily from under her bedclothes. She threw Vicki a sullen glance. 'I'm sorry, I just can't keep an eye on him every minute of the night and day, but I don't suppose he's any further than the kitchen!'

Alarm quickened Vicki's footsteps as she turned and fled. She didn't even stop to tell Miss Webb what she thought of her, letting a four-year-old out of her sight like this! It wasn't until she found Graham that she calmed down. It wasn't, after all, Miss Webb's fault. She couldn't be expected to be on duty the whole time, as she had pointed out, and Graham had never been a boy to sleep much. Only the freedom of the station could be going to his head after the necessary restrictions of one room.

This, Vicki thought resentfully, was where a father might have helped out—a normal father, that was. If Wade had been a normal father he might have kept an adventurous young son happy in the mornings—at least, for an hour. He could have taken him out, perhaps to the stock pens or to watch the men setting out on their daily work. But Wade wasn't, she thought angrily, any normal father. He hadn't any interest in his son at all.

Graham was in the kitchen, laughing and chattering to an aborigine girl, while another was giving him coffee.

Vicki, alarmed, almost snatched this from him. 'You don't have that, darling! You have milk, or even milky chocolate!' She felt so hurt that he hadn't come and sought her, she let more anger show in her voice than she had intended.

The aborigine girls stared at her, their dark eyes round with fright, but before they could speak, two hands tightly clasped her bare arms from behind and Wade spoke over her shoulder.

'Coffee won't hurt him once in a while. I was almost

reared on the stuff and it hasn't done me any harm. Don't fuss, Victoria!'

Graham immediately went into boyish giggles about her full name, which he had seldom heard before. What he came out with, after several tries, sounded very much like the wistaria which grew up walls, but she seemed to have lost her sense of humour. Wade must have been behind her when she had expected he would be outside.

Graham stopped chortling as suddenly as he'd began.

'Graham likes coffee,' he stuck out his lower lip defiantly. Vicki hadn't realised it was becoming such a habit and made a mental note to speak to him about it—if she could persuade him to take any notice! 'Daddy drinks coffee, so Graham can,' he cried crossly.

'I can,' Vicki corrected feebly, wondering whether to correct him about the Daddy bit too. A boy of his age couldn't be expected to remember everything right away, although, from the look in his eyes, she had a horrid suspicion he hadn't really forgotten what Wade had told him about that. Impulsively she decided to say nothing. Wade could straighten him out himself on that point, if he thought it worth making a fuss about. As Graham scowled she introduced a note of firmness. 'That's not to say, darling, milk wouldn't be better for you. After all, you're only four.' As he went on sulking she tried to twist from Wade's tightening grip. 'Will you let me go, please?' she asked coldly when she failed.

He refused, cruelly enjoying the agitation she tried to hide. 'Why aren't you still in bed?' he queried, with a matching coldness. 'I was just about to bring your breakfast—a concession until you're stronger.' As he spoke his breath came down against her cheek. Quickly, an inarticulate sound in her throat, Vicki averted her head.

Suddenly it came to her why he was here, why he had been going to bring her breakfast. He hadn't been going to risk having anyone see where she was sleeping! 'You don't have to run after me,' she muttered bitterly. 'You must have forgotten I never liked having breakfast in bed. Unlike your lady visitors, I've never been used to it.'

His hands dug into her, then slackened, but not before she'd felt in them the desire to hurt. 'You don't have to remind me, but I also remember you did once like it there, when I joined you.'

How dared he remind her of that! That one morning, after ... Indignantly she broke her thoughts, turning in a flash to face him, which was a mistake. Finding him too near, she edged towards Graham, hiding her scarlet face. 'I'll see to Graham's breakfast, then get my own,' she murmured frigidly.

Wade merely stared at her frostily, looking aggressively masculine in his checked bush shirt and tight-fitting fawn pants. 'The girls here have already given Graham his breakfast, but you're at liberty to help yourself, if you insist. This is Misilgoe and Boalere,' he nodded towards them, with a faint smile, and they stopped looking apprehensive. 'They're new to the house since you were here.'

After Vicki said good morning, rather shakily, he told them to take Graham upstairs. Like the previous evening, he abruptly dismissed the boy when he began protesting. 'Leave him with Miss Webb. She'll look after him.'

'No!' Vicki objected, seeing the last remnants of her authority dwindling before her very eyes. 'Please stop!' As the two girls grabbed Graham and disappeared without taking any notice, she turned back to Wade, her blue eyes brilliant with anger.

'Your dedication to duty is touching,' he sneered, 'but I'd appreciate it more if you left him to Miss Webb. I think you should conserve your energy for other things.'

'Do you?' she challenged sharply. 'That's because you don't know what it feels like to be a normal parent! To me, looking after Graham is a pleasure. He's not just something to be shoved off with relief on to a nanny.'

'You have to have time to recover.' His dark face was

hard as he looked her over. 'You're looking very charming this morning, almost as enticing as you did last night. If you have any energy to spare you can reserve it for me. If I'm to keep three extra people for several weeks I might demand some kind of compensation.'

'How do you mean?' she cried.

'I'll allow you to work that out for yourself,' he replied, as coolly as if he was discussing market prices.

Vicki, lifting her face quickly, as suspicious fear lanced through her, was wholly unprepared when his arms caught her and his mouth found hers.

His mouth was as cruel as it had been the night before and even more insulting. He kissed her as if she was a machine to be used, when and how he needed her. His lips parted hers insolently and his body went taut against her weakening limbs, reviving her memory. His sensual assault was contemptuous, yet the warm desire within her to respond was so strong she felt her senses swimming.

Then, just as suddenly as he had taken her, he pushed her away, having no obvious pity for the way she shrank from him, the manner in which she moved shaken fingers over her mouth, her wide, pale brow. 'You asked,' his voice cooled maliciously, 'and I've supplied a clue, that's all. I might reach the point of wondering why the hell I should entertain other women when I have a wife available.'

She stared up into his detached face, into the eyes which, in spite of his having held her so close only a moment ago, held nothing but aversion. 'You must be mad,' she whispered, her voice barely audible in the silent kitchen, 'if you think you're going to get anything from me! I didn't ask to come here, not to stay, anyway. I only wanted to collect my son. If you insist on keeping us on Baccaroo then it's your own fault if you feel inconvenienced or out of pocket.'

His mouth firmed and his eyes were chill. 'You've a sharper tongue than you used to have, madam. You must see that it's not quite so sharp when others are around. If·

you want to avoid speculation by giving the impression of reconciliation, then you must be prepared to play your part. I can't do it alone.'

'I can be civil,' she hissed, her cheeks flaring scarlet, 'just as long as you don't expect me to continue being over-polite when we're alone. Or over-anything!' she finished, incomprehensibly, only wishing she had some means of making him feel as nervous as he made her.

That he was angry she could tell from the grim set of his mouth. Grasping her arm again, he baited her further. 'You're not entirely indifferent—I sensed it last night. I'm also aware of some change in you that it might pay me to investigate.'

'I never thought you'd sink low enough to remind me of that!' She referred to what had taken place when she'd gone seeking blankets. Suddenly incensed, she struck out at him with her free hand, hitting him across his disdainful face. The force of it made red marks on the hardness of his cheek. 'I'm not sorry!' she exclaimed, her voice rising. 'You deserve to suffer more than that. You give me a terrible room . . .'

'And?' he prompted silkily, as she faltered, helplessly infuriated with herself that she had betrayed what little pride she had left by complaining.

'Well, I don't know how you could,' she muttered, with childish truculence, feeling completely unnerved.

Wade McLeod's anger rose as hers dropped. 'I'm not here to account for everything which enters your empty little mind. You'll stay there as long as you intend sleeping alone. But I'm not holding any gun to your head, or hinting that I'd welcome you with open arms. If your bedroom doesn't come up to your expectations, you might stop to consider if you deserve any better.'

'Oh, all right!' Vicki tried desperately to cover a fresh flood of fury with a meekness she was far from feeling. She was only sorry she had said anything. She hadn't meant to. Wade might be unfair—she didn't know how he could feel justified in saying half the things he had, but there could be little sense in standing here insulting each other. When it came to an open battle of words, Wade would most probably win, as he'd usually done! She would be wiser to bide her time. Besides, the girls might appear at any moment and Miss Webb certainly hadn't had her breakfast, if everyone else had. Vicki remembered she hadn't yet eaten herself.

She took a deep breath. 'I'll soon get my room cleaned up. I take it you won't object to my doing that? I'd hate to think I was disturbing happy old memories, along with the dust!'

'Why, you——' Then, like herself, he subsided. 'Get the girls to do that,' he allowed carefully, his grey eyes glinting.

'Wade,' she hesitated, hoping to divert the conversation to a less controversial topic, 'I feel awfully sorry about poor Mrs Clover. After you told me I thought about her quite a bit. You say she died. I hope she didn't suffer?'

'No.' Wade didn't remark on the sudden tears in Vicki's eyes, but his glance softened slightly. 'It was a heart attack. She only lived an hour afterwards. By the time the flying doc got here it was all over. Not that he could have done anything, supposing he'd been on the spot. Before she went she spoke of you.'

This last bit of information being given so grudgingly, Vicki didn't pursue it. For a minute she couldn't trust herself to speak. 'I'm sorry,' she repeated. 'I know how long she was with you.' She wondered what he would say if she were to tell him about all the stories Mrs Clover had been so fond of relating about his childhood, all the questions Vicki had asked, the way she had listened. Instead she said softly, while Wade nodded curtly, 'I'm going to miss her. Who do you have now in her place?'

'No one but the two girls you saw. We did have someone, but she left, just before we heard of you again. I've not got around to replacing her.'

Vicki didn't ask why the last woman hadn't stayed. It

might have been a simple matter of loneliness. The isolation of the Outback defeated many. 'You mean you've only got two girls? No one in charge of them?'

'Nope.'

His laconic drawl wasn't helpful. Vicki knew, from experience, the aborigine women were not very good in the house. Outside, on the stations, the aborigine men made splendid stockmen, but in the homestead their women often needed constant supervision. It maybe had to do with the fact that the aborigines had become too used to living in old huts of corrugated iron where there had been little housework to be done. Even today, with improved conditions, their cooking was often done outside on campfires and there was little to encourage them to excel in the domestic arts. Some of the station owners' wives found it easier to do the housework themselves, although Mrs Clover had never been deterred.

Vicki glanced at Wade doubtfully. 'Were these girls here with Mrs Clover? I mean, are they trained? If not, then who's been looking after your grandfather, and Miss Webb?'

'God!' Wade ran an impatient hand around the back of his head. 'Haven't I enough to do without having to bother about things like that? The last housekeeper we had managed to train Misilgoe. I expect it was she who cooked our dinner last night.'

'It wasn't very appetising.'

'I didn't notice.'

What had he noticed, then? Vicki recalled his dark unreadable face. Certainly she had come in for some attention, if none of it approving. She didn't flatter herself she'd been enough to take his mind off a badly cooked meal.

'Wade,' she looked at him levelly, her eyes wide-spaced and very clear, 'you've been hinting about having to keep Graham and me. More, I suspect, to annoy me than anything else, but I intend paying my way by taking over here. You refuse to get rid of Miss Webb. If your grandfather is as ill as you say then perhaps a nurse might be good to have around. But this aside, it doesn't take two women to look after one small boy, and I can't sit around doing nothing all day.'

His jaw went tight. 'Damn it, girl, don't you ever give up? You're going to concentrate on getting your strength back, not on my domestic problems!'

'So you can send me back to Melbourne as good as new,' she rejoined bitterly. 'When the time comes, no matter what I do, I can assure you I'll go without any fuss.'

'Well, I don't want you here.'

He could mean on the station, but she found it wasn't so hurtful to settle for the kitchen. 'Won't people think it strange if I'm not here, seeing how you're placed?'

'You're still far from well.'

'I don't intend wearing myself out, if that's what you mean. I'll take things easy—to begin with, anyway.'

'Please yourself.' His voice was cutting as he shrugged his broad shoulders. 'But if you must amuse yourself in this way don't blame me if you kill yourself. Maybe it will save me the trouble of getting rid of you, if you're whipped off to hospital again.'

Vicki swallowed. 'Then you won't be advertising for another housekeeper?'

'I'll reserve judgment on that,' he retorted flatly. 'I refuse to promise you anything, other than the edge of my tongue if you don't keep your son out of my sight!'

After breakfast was over, Vicki tried to put the hurt in her heart aside and see her present position in its proper perspective. Once she had restored some sort of order in the kitchen she went in search of old Mr McLeod. Miss Webb, she had been informed by the lady herself, had worked out a routine for Graham which she didn't want broken. Which she doesn't want me breaking, Vicki thought dismally, as Miss Webb whisked Graham away. She knew she might have asserted herself, but she supposed he was in need of a little discipline after years of Mrs Parkes, and

Miss Webb didn't seem such a terrible dragon. She was only a determined young woman, trying to make her presence felt.

Vicki realised that if she was to survive the next few weeks she must learn to relax her over-possessive hold on Graham a little. She must learn not to be so over-anxious every minute of the day. If she learnt to let go, especially when he was in such capable hands, both she and Graham might benefit. She had to convince herself this would be so, but it wasn't easy. Having had sole charge of him since he was born, she had had to learn to make every decision, a habit which she might find difficult to change. Briefly she wondered what it would have been like if Graham had been born here, at Baccaroo, and she had had Wade at her side to help and advise during these important, formative years. Maybe by now they might have had another child to keep Graham company. Feeling her cheeks grow hot, Vicki immediately dismissed such a thought and tried to concentrate on her more pressing problems.

Ruefully she knew she had been trying to persuade herself that Graham was better out of the way because she wasn't sure she could cope with him and all she wanted to do that morning. She had argued otherwise with Wade, but already she was beginning to realise she hadn't regained her usual energy. She must conserve what she had. Her room, she decided, was urgent, but meals were obviously the more important. Dust could wait, but a man's hunger was another thing. Then she must see old Mr McLeod and have a few things out with him, if she dared!

Crossing the hall, she found the huge house quiet, already beginning to drowse in the steadily mounting heat of the day. Miss Webb had borne Graham off for a walk down by the creek where, so she had informed Vicki, she was teaching him to count with the aid of various birds. It had seemed simple enough, and interesting, but Vicki missed having him around with his noisy chatter.

She paused a moment in the drawing room when she

didn't find old Mr McLeod there. It could be a lovely house. She could have improved it a lot after she had married Wade, but he had refused to allow her to touch anything. This hadn't been because he hadn't thought her capable; it had been because of the situation between him and his grandfather—a state of affairs which she could see hadn't altered much.

Wade had told her, though, shortly after they had married, that his mother had built the house. His mother had apparently come from a wealthy Sydney family. On top of this she had inherited a considerable sum of money from two aunts. The old house still stood, but appeared very primitive compared with this. When his mother had died it was found she had left everything to her only child and, when Wade had grown up, he had used it to increase the McLeod holdings. Vicki believed he was the largest shareholder. She didn't think, however, in spite of the bad feeling between his grandfather and him, that he had ever needed to use this power as the Old Man seemed quite willing to let him make almost every decision.

What had she hoped for, Vicki wondered wistfully, this mother of Wade's who had died before her son was properly grown? What would she think now, if she could come back, to see and feel the unhappiness and bitterness at Baccaroo? In the house she had probably meant to fill only with love and laughter.

Vicki eventually found the Old Man in the main office, a building set some way from the house.

'For a girl who's taken to fainting all over the place, you're up and about early enough,' he grunted, when she appeared in the doorway.

'I don't think I'll be doing that any more, Mr McLeod,' she replied. From the way his eyes narrowed she knew he was wondering why she didn't continue calling him Grandfather. Well, she never would, not until he asked her, and this he had never done, probably never would. Coolly she looked at him, trying not to allow her gaze to wander around the room which had once been so familiar. Hadn't she been here when Wade had come seeking her, on the day he had asked her to marry him? She clenched her hands, shutting off her thoughts, and spoke quickly to his grandfather. 'I'm going to try and make myself useful around the house, so I came to see if you would like coffee. Misilgoe mentioned that you usually have it in the drawing room, these days, and rest afterwards.'

'What I'm reduced to,' he snarled, without offering an explanation. Then, as Vicki made no reply, 'Why should you want to make me coffee, girl, after the way I bawled at you in Melbourne?'

'Is this an apology, Mr McLeod?' Vicki glanced at him wryly, unable to think for a moment that it was.

She was right. 'No, just curiosity,' he retorted shortly.

The overseer came in, but halted abruptly when coming face to face with Vicki. He was a man in his early thirties, expert at everything but so nice with it that his smartness never jarred. Vicki had liked him; she still did. He had always been pleasant to her, and oddly protective, especially before she had married Wade. That her marriage had been a small shock to him she had guessed, although to what extent she had never known.

Now, although paling slightly, he smiled at her warmly. 'I'm pleased to see you back, Vicki.'

She didn't doubt his sincerity as she shook his hand. He didn't seem surprised at finding her here, so she supposed Wade must have told him she had returned.

Jeff Curry didn't pretend not to be studying her keenly, but made no personal comment on her over-fragile appearance, although his smile faded as he looked her over. Instead he spoke of Graham. 'You've got a really fine youngster there, Vicki. Old Ned was saying he's exactly as Wade was at his age. And Ned should know.'

Why can't someone say he's a bit like me? Vicki stifled such a retort and kept a smile pinned on her lips.

The Old Man interrupted. 'I'm going back to the house,

Jeff. I reckon I'm not much help here, anyhow. I've just been talking to Ada Court, from Montgoora. They were delighted with my great-grandson when they were over the night before last. She was just enquiring if Wade was back.'

Vicki felt her lips tighten as she followed him out. The whole Territory would have known Wade was back, almost as soon as he flew in. And his wife with him! They apparently, at least some of them had, lost no time in coming to look Graham over. Were they awaiting further developments? Vicki had never found it so herself, but a lot of people found life in the Outback occasionally monotonous and uneventful. Without their battery-operated transceivers, which many of them listened to regularly, they would find their days very dull indeed.

With the news out that Wade McLeod's missing wife had returned with a son, people would be visiting. Few of them could have any idea of the true circumstances, and their neighbours, being mostly kind-hearted to a fault, would make a great fuss of Graham. Graham, young though he was, or perhaps because he was so young, would lap it all up. When the time came it might be impossible to tear him away. A feeling of despair rose inside her.

After the Old Man went! Frowning, as she poured his coffee, Vicki pondered on the best way to discover the exact condition of his heart. The opportunity came more easily than she had expected.

'So you're going to try taking up where Annie Clover left off?' He drank from his cup noisily, not looking at her.

'I don't think I'll be able to do that, exactly,' Vicki replied cautiously, 'but there can't be any harm in trying.'

'Oh, you were always one for trying,' he retorted harshly. 'Give you an inch and you'd take a mile, as I soon discovered. You connived to get in where you were never wanted.'

When she made no reply apart from taking a deep breath and clenching her fingers, he rumbled on with a strange change of tone, 'All my life others have worked against me, and I only had their interests at heart.'

'You mean you only thought of Baccaroo!'

'Same thing, isn't it?' His bushy eyebrows in his lined old face drew together.

'Not exactly . . .'

'I miss Annie Clover,' the increasing harshness in his voice might have hid emotion. 'She was a good woman, when she made the effort.'

'You liked her because she never attempted to assert herself, but that didn't mean she was blind to what went on.'

He ignored the last part of her sentence. 'Hardly her place to assert herself, young woman.'

'Nor mine? Are you trying to issue a sort of warning, Mr McLeod?'

'Annie Clover probably saved my life.' He stared past Vicki's head as if he were seeing another scene, if reluctantly. 'I owe her . . .'

Vicki took it he was referring to some incident from his youth. 'It's a bit late, isn't it?'

'Yes,' for a moment his eyes closed and his mouth compressed, 'far too late. I wasn't able to speak to her before she died.'

Puzzled, Vicki asked why not.

'Because,' he cleared his throat and glared at her, as if only impatient, 'of all the damn fool things, I took a turn when I saw she'd taken one! Annie wasn't far short of me in years, but she was younger, so I guess it was a shock to see her lying there. Only a fool wouldn't have known she was done for. Anyway, when that fool of a doctor flew in he said I'd had a heart attack too, but not as bad as Annie's. He said Annie's collapse had likely saved my life, that I could have had a much worse attack anywhere and been a goner before I'd got help. Now I have these miraculous tablets, girl. I take two and, suppose I say it myself, they're real good.'

So Wade had been telling the truth about his grandfather's heart. Her own problems momentarily forgotten, Vicki stared at him almost sadly. Whatever else he had been, the Old Man was a fighter. Still was, if the glint in his eye was anything to go by, and for this she respected him. Something dejected about him, as he resumed his staring into space, caught at her heart, until she realised he had never invited sympathy. He probably wouldn't know what to do with it. Hadn't he always brushed any show of affection aside as if it was to be mistrusted? Well, at least she knew now about his heart. 'I'm sorry,' she muttered dully, becoming aware that the Old Man's health had put an end to her immediate hopes of escaping with Graham.

She was on the point of getting unhappily to her feet when Mr McLeod spoke again.

# CHAPTER FIVE

'THEY won't keep me alive for ever,' Vicki was startled to hear the Old Man say. 'Wade and Doc Evans think me a fool, but I know my time is almost up. Just as long as I live to see Wade married to a proper wife.'

Vicki stood up abruptly. 'I'm sure you'll do that, Mr McLeod.' Crushing a sudden panic under anger, she warned him sharply, 'But don't think you'll be able to get rid of me and keep my son!'

'Wade needs more sons.' The Old Man didn't look pathetic any more, his mouth set stubbornly. 'I think I know the very girl for him.'

'Surely you're running out of suitable candidates, Mr McLeod? Why not give up and let Wade choose for himself? He's old enough.'

This observation seemed to disturb the Old Man to such an extent that his face went red. As Vicki's eyes widened with alarmed dismay, his high colour faded to a ghastly white and he gave a funny little gasp and slumped sideways.

With a presence of mind she was far from feeling, Vicki asked quickly, 'Where are your tablets?'

'Here,' he groped for his pocket clumsily and she carefully pushed his hand aside to extract them.

She gave him two with some lukewarm coffee, holding the cup to his lips carefully as he was unable to lift it himself. In a very few seconds he recovered a little, and the bluish tinge around his mouth disappeared.

'Don't think you've saved my life, girl, like Annie did,' he gasped, when he was able to speak. 'I'm well used to managing myself when this thing hits me. It's easier when someone's around, that's all.'

'Yes, I understand.' Vicki stared down at him anxiously,

the acid taste of near-defeat in her mouth, convinced now
she couldn't tackle him about anything much. She wouldn't
want to be responsible for another attack like this, no matter
what happened. She must resign herself to having to face
the enemy without being able to fight back. There was still
Wade, of course. Somehow she must find a way of defeat-
ing him so his grandfather would suffer no ill effects.

After sitting with him quietly for a while and satisfying
herself he was recovered, Vicki returned to the kitchen. Her
morning's schedule was well behind time and she felt herself growing agitated. In the kitchen she found yet another cause for dismay. Misilgoe was there, alone, and
only half of Vicki's orders had been carried out.

'Boalere says to tell Missus she come back later,' Misilgoe
said stolidly.

'Later!' Vicki snapped, feeling, that for one morning, she
had had about enough. Then, seeing the recurring alarm
on Misilgoe's face, 'Oh, well, I imagine between the two
of us we can manage lunch.'

'Boss come back?'

'No. That is, I don't suppose so.' He had rarely been in
for lunch in the old days, but things might have changed.
'Does he usually?' she tried to ask casually.

'Sometimes, since Old Man got bad ticker,' Misilgoe replied carelessly.

Could this be because he cared? Vicki hadn't thought
either Wade or his grandfather could confuse her further,
but it seemed they could. 'I see,' she smiled slightly at the
girl, trying not to reveal that the news wasn't welcome. She
had planned to concentrate on dinner, rather than the mid-
day meal. She must get her room done and, understanding
Wade's silent warning, she must do this discreetly. She
could have done with Boalere's help, but perhaps it was
just as well she was out of the way.

Perspiration beaded her brow and body, making her thin
dress cling. Impatiently she wondered why her strength
didn't return faster. There was still almost the whole day

to be got through, and already she felt ready to collapse.

Giving the impression, without resorting to deliberate lies, she pretended she had upset something, and gathering a bucket and dusters went upstairs. Breathless before she reached the top, she wished fervently that Wade's mother had built the usual Outback bungalow type of house instead of a two-storey affair.

Two hours later she had almost completed everything she had set out to do and stood back to survey her handiwork. The bedroom didn't look much different, but it was greatly improved. All the dust had gone and the paintings had been washed and cleaned, the floor scrubbed. Clean linen covered the bed and she had found a pair of lacy curtains, but these would have to wait until another day. She had no strength left to hang them herself, although she had managed to remove the old torn ones from the window.

Horrified to discover herself so tired she could scarcely move, she sank on to the chair beside the bed, deciding she might be wiser to remain where she was until she recovered a little. She felt thankful she had told Misilgoe not to disturb her. As she sat, she heard Graham's childish treble floating up from the garden and old Mr McLeod's deeper, answering tones. The Old Man must have recovered. Vicki felt relieved but also envious that he could join Graham and Miss Webb, while her legs felt so weak again she dared not even try to.

There came the sounds of lunch, the distant clatter of plates and cutlery from the kitchens, then Graham going to his room for his afternoon rest. Vicki felt hurt that he hadn't come searching for her. He had probably been forbidden to when it was supposed she was resting and he seemed happy enough, if his bright chatter was anything to go by. She dared not call to him as he went past her door for fear Miss Webb saw what room she was in. After this there was silence, a long, quiet interlude which she passed by worrying about almost everything, punctuating each fresh problem she thought of with hopeless little prayers for a cup of tea.

When the door opened abruptly she wasn't prepared to find Wade striding in, holding one in his hand. Feeling rather like Aladdin with his lamp, she stared at him, unaware how her white face, covered with streaks of dust, reminded him of the day he had found her in her room in Melbourne.

'What the devil!' he exploded, closing the door behind him, with an almost identical bang. 'What the hell have you been up to now?'

'I've only been cleaning my room,' she replied stiffly, not attempting to evade the issue, adding with a dignity belied by a faint tremor in her voice, 'As it's really your dressing room and was much in need of a good scrub out, you shouldn't object.'

'That needles you, doesn't it?' He put down the cup he carried sharply on the low table by her side. 'You're still annoyed I didn't offer you my bed as well as your board. Well, let me tell you, girl, it took long enough to eradicate the image of your exotic little body from my pillows four years ago. I wouldn't go to the same trouble again, not unless you were to be there permanently.'

As she stared at him wordlessly, wondering whether that was a statement or query, or something else again, her face seemed to go even paler.

This brought another snarling exclamation. 'Look at you! Almost ready to drop. I've seen more life in a baby calf after it had been savaged by a wild dog. There was no need to start on this today.'

'I'm quite all right!' Weakly she considered his comparisons might be appropriate. The two men in this house, for all their civilised urbanity, did remind her sometimes of the savage wild beasts Wade referred to. 'I'm just having a rest,' she protested.

His face couldn't have been colder, or more uncaring. 'Listen, Vicki, I've told you, I don't care if you want to kill yourself, but you won't do it while you're staying here.'

The pain of that stabbed, but she tried to ignore it. 'You agreed this morning that I could do as I liked.'

'When I said you could take over the house I didn't mean like this. I've just been hearing about what you've been up to, both here and in the office. My grandfather tells me Jeff almost swooned at the sight of you. During the next few weeks I'd advise you to keep out of Jeff's way. I don't want you running to him like you used to do, with your complaints!'

'It wasn't like that and you know it!' she gasped. 'I talked to him sometimes, that was all.'

'Jeff's always been half in love with you. Deny that, if you can? The Old Man——'

'Your grandfather, Wade!' she broke in sharply, disregarding his cold expression as anxiety struck her. 'Is he all right? I don't know how I forgot.'

'Sure,' Wade's voice was clipped. 'He's out, right now, with Jeff as a matter of fact. Stop worrying about him.'

She had never intended worrying, yet was surprised to hear herself cry indignantly, 'Someone ought to!'

'Not you. Take a look at yourself!' Fury edged his voice. 'Come on, into bed before I lose my temper completely.'

'No!' She was aware, from his glittering eyes, that his control was slipping, but she must defy him. It was like a battle from which she could see no way of making a dignified retreat. 'No, I won't,' she repeated stubbornly, while every one of her aching bones just cried out for the rest he advised.

As if tried beyond everything by her time-wasting procrastinations, Wade bent down from his great height and took hold of her. Before she could say another word he had lifted her on to the bed and began undoing the buttons on the front of her dress. 'I'm your husband,' he snapped, 'if only for the next few weeks, and with a child you're surely a very much married woman. So we'll have no more of your childish protests. It's not as if I had anything else in mind but the necessity of getting you into bed.'

Giving in at last, because of the frightening surge of feeling that went through her, in spite of her weakened state, when he touched her, she struggled feebly and said she could manage—would manage, if he left her, but he appeared to be past taking any notice. He slipped the dress from her shoulders, his hands too lean and strong to be pushed aside. Utterly humiliated, she felt herself lifted as he removed it completely, leaving her sitting there shivering with nerves, in her brief underclothes.

Her bra, just a silken scrap of material, scarcely covered the high, rounded curves of a figure which was no longer that of a young girl, and was emphasised by the extreme slenderness of her waist. Below her waist the fine bones of her hips were slight, but behind these more pronounced curves of flesh appeared seductively enticing. Attempting to cover herself and hide her burning embarrassment, she drew up her long, slender legs and began wrapping her bare arms around them.

Wade wasn't having any. For a moment he stood staring at her and she saw a dark red creeping along his taut jaw line. A peculiar floating sensation hit her and she didn't think she breathed. Suddenly she wanted to raise her tightly clasped arms and hold them out to him, to lose herself entirely in the smouldering caverns of his dark, narrowed eyes.

When his hands lifted again she thought, for one black, pulse-racing moment, that he was going to drag her to him, to relieve his masculine feelings as urgently as he had once done in the past. Instead she found herself almost thrust beneath the blankets, with a dexterity she found difficult to follow, and Wade was striding into the bathroom.

'Stay there,' he commanded curtly, his body noticeably tense when he came back with a damp flannel. This he passed to her. 'You can rub your face with this until you're able to make the bathroom yourself. After you've cleaned up you can drink your tea and stay where you are for at least the remainder of the afternoon.'

Vicki obeyed wordlessly, for once, but was unable to look at him. Things seemed to be pressing painfully on her subconsciousness, as if waiting to be released, but as before, she didn't yet feel able to face them.

Unable to read her remote face, Wade let out a sigh of impatience as he left her. Five minutes later, however, just when the tearful feeling of being deserted was going, he surprised her by returning with a plate of soup.

'Out of a tin,' he told her, 'but none the worse for that. You could have mentioned that you hadn't had lunch.'

After he had finally gone Vicki ate the soup, astonished to find she was hungry. Knowing this must be a sure sign of returning health, she felt slightly happier as she lay back against cool, clean pillows and drowsily watched transparent rays of glistening sunlight playing on the opposite wall. Seeing no curtains at the window, Wade hadn't offered to hang the pair which lay waiting, but he had draped a dark sheet half over the glass to keep out the worst of the burning sun. There was no wind, no sound her mind could contemplate in the soft silence around her. She tried to think about Graham but felt her thoughts clinging wholly to her husband. Uneasily she wondered why he should suddenly be becoming more important to her than her son.

Wade had told her he had to go out again, although she wasn't sure why he had told her this. Even if things had been different between them she wouldn't have expected him to stay in. The boss, as the owner of a cattle station was usually known in the Outback, had to be a man with definite qualities, not least among them being a strong will to survive, a tough physique; iron nerves and a good knowledge of self-defence. In Wade McLeod there were all these qualities and more, but it was this hardness which still defeated her.

He had brought her tea and soup and, she supposed, in his way, been kind to her, but this must only disguise a disinclination to have another invalid on his hands. It must

be up to her to prove she was far from sickly, but, with the
feeling of his hands still on her, she found her thoughts
growing wistful.

She dozed then woke, to find her thoughts continuing
exactly where they had left off. In Melbourne she had
been usually too busy to do much thinking and, at night,
too exhausted to do anything but fall into a dreamless sleep.
Now, for the first time in years, it seemed she had time to
reflect but was reluctant to do so. For all she tried to occupy
herself with other things she always returned to Wade.

Being in the office that morning had somehow taken
her sharply back to the evening he had asked her to marry
him. She wondered if any girl had ever received a stranger
proposal. It must certainly have been unusual, with Wade,
her would-be fiancé, in a terrible temper, and she herself
too frightened to be able to say no.

He had been slamming on the brakes of a Land-Rover
when she had glanced up startled from the letter she had
been typing. It was for the Old Man and she should have
had it done earlier in the day, but she had been helping
Mrs Clover.

'Oh, hello,' she had said uncertainly, very young and very
nervous as he had crashed in through the door. She didn't
suppose she had ever looked plainer, with her hair only an
hour ago sheared even shorter, in the vain hope that
it would help her feel cooler, her face devoid of make-up
and a shabby shirt clinging to over-thin shoulders.

He had towered above her, all six foot two of him, deeply
tanned and lean with grey eyes and smooth dark hair, dis-
tinguished in a disturbing way. He hadn't asked if it was
convenient, or if she was busy, which she obviously was.
He had simply stood looking at her for some extremely long
moments before ordering her to come with him.

'But why?' she had gathered enough courage to falter,
already more aware of him than she cared to admit. She
had been ever since he had kissed her, although she had
tried to convince herself she had forgotten all about it.

'Don't argue, Vicki!' he had dismissed her nervous query ruthlessly as he had grasped her arm, the steely hardness of his voice and fingers conveying more than a hint of his inner fury.

Apprehensively she hadn't seemed able to prevent him from almost thrusting her into the waiting vehicle. She had shrunk into a corner but stayed silent as he had driven swiftly down across the creek, over plains and down gullies, up hillsides covered by what seemed to her dangerous loose pebbles until, at the edge of another dried up creek, he had stopped. As if he had managed to get rid of a little of his anger by such rough driving, he had pulled up in the shade of some trees which in turn were overshadowed by one of the huge red boulders which had once formed part of a mountain range.

There he had turned, after switching off the engine, and asked her to marry him. In the blank silence which followed she remembered thinking this must be something which happened every day, but nowhere, she guessed, could there have been a more businesslike proposal!

In the brief lead up to it, he asked abruptly if she liked living here. The question might have sounded casual, but as he had spoken to her he had stared at her closely, as if her answer was all-important. She had been glad to be able to say truthfully that she loved it. It was, she had sensed, what he wanted to hear, but she had had to search harder when he had asked her why. Eventually she had to confess that she wasn't sure. As she blinked at him doubtfully, wildly exaggerated reasons had flashed through her bewildered head, seeming all the more fanciful because they were true. In the end she had just shaken her head and said helplessly, 'Because I do.'

Somehow that short sentence, uttered so compulsively, had seemed to convince him more than a feverish flow of words might have done. He had apparently been satisfied, for it was then that he had asked her to marry him. Vicki could still recall the leashed impatience in his voice, the glitter in his eyes which had convinced her instinctively that he would rather have ordered than asked, if he had thought he could have got away with it.

Vicki had found herself trembling under his grim, waiting appraisal. It had been difficult at first to believe he could be serious. Wade McLeod, who could perhaps have his pick of the women in the Territory, proposing to Vicki Neilson who was, without doubt, a plain little nobody. Why, his grandfather would throw a fit, and she couldn't altogether blame him!

Wide-eyed, she gazed at him. 'Why me, of all people?' she had whispered. 'You——' she had found it difficult to go on but it had to be said, 'you don't love me, and you know so many really beautiful women.' Briefly, as a sudden pain struck her, she had closed her eyes.

'I'll tell you why I want you for my wife, Vicki,' Wade had said curtly, 'and you can open those huge blue eyes of yours and look as shocked as you like. It's because I'm sick to my very soul of the way my grandfather continually parades these women whom you consider so beautiful in front of me. Prospective wives to meet the future needs of Baccaroo. He knows I don't intend marrying because of the past, but he never lets up. I never know who's going to turn up next. He insists on disrupting my life unceasingly. Someone is coming tomorrow whom I've no particular fancy to entertain, and I'm determined to put an end to it. I believe marrying someone like you is the only possible way.'

Vicki had been struck speechless by that for a moment. Her poise, never very secure when this devastating man was around, deserted her. At last she had turned up her face to him, her eyes indeed enormous. 'Sometimes you seem to like talking to these women.' It was as good as admitting she watched him, but she had felt too strung up to care.

'I'm only human, Vicki,' he'd replied cynically. 'I find it difficult to be less than polite, and occasionally see no reason to deprive myself of what's often so freely offered, with no strings attached.'

She had frowned, not knowing quite what to make of that. 'One of these days you might feel tempted to marry one of them, if you wait. You might——' she hesitated, wondering why it should seem so ridiculous to suggest to Wade McLeod that he might possibly come to really care for somebody. 'You might fall in love.'

'Not a chance.' His mouth had twisted derisively. 'I don't believe in it, for one thing, and I'm determined to avoid any kind of warmer relationship for another. You must trust me to know what I'm doing, Vicki.'

Because he was older and consequently vastly more experienced, she felt he must be right. Love was a thing for books, the imagination, not for everyday life. At best it might only be a strong physical attraction. A man as bitter and hard as Wade McLeod might not even set much store by that.

As she nodded silently to his last comment he spoke with such emphatic coldness she shrank. 'I'm going to marry you, Vicki, if only to see the look on the Old Man's face, not because I have any particular feelings for you.'

'Wade!' Vicki's face had paled before such a cold-blooded declaration, but she dared whisper, 'Mrs Clover told me a little about your family history. Don't you think it's about time you forgave your grandfather? I don't say forget, but I think if you were to take a fresh look at what happened, through adult eyes, you might understand his anxiety. After all, you were very young when your father died, too young perhaps to appreciate that your grandfather's motives, through mistaken, were only human.'

'Shut up!' Wade retorted, very coldly and crisply. 'If you're quite finished! We won't talk of this again, if you don't mind. A man in his thirties doesn't have to listen to advice from foolish little girls. In future it will pay you to remember.'

She had laughed, then, on a note of rising hysteria, with

anger bringing feverish waves of colour to her cheeks, giving her, had she but known it, a kind of transient beauty which, for a moment, appeared to narrow his eyes warily. 'This must be one of the strangest proposals a girl has ever had to listen to,' she had cried.

It had been the wrong thing to say. It certainly hadn't disconcerted him. He had simply stared at her, as if she was the one being unreasonable. 'But this isn't an ordinary proposal. You realise, Vicki, ours wouldn't be a normal marriage?'

'Well, I won't marry you, either way.'

His mouth had merely curled in contempt. His hands had reached for her shoulders as if he wanted to shake sense into her—and quickly. In his eyes she had seen her own distress reflected clearly in the cold, icy grey. 'If you don't marry me, what have you to go back to?' he had asked harshly. 'No job, no home, your nearest relations, if you have any, in England.'

'You've been checking!'

'Why not? An eye for detail has always given me what I wanted, in the end.'

Vicki stirred restlessly on the hard bed, wishing she could sleep, so she might black out the shameful memory of how easily she had capitulated. Eventually she hadn't been able to face a future as empty as he had pointed out and, in agreeing to marry him, she had managed to convince herself that her motives were no more selfish than his. Most of all, though, she hadn't been able to resist the temptation of being able to stay on at Baccaroo. And with Wade! Unhappily she acknowledged, now, that she had already been half in love with him, only she hadn't realised that until it was too late.

A week later they had been married. They had flown into Alice Springs and there, in the Centre, as Alice was popularly known, she had become Mrs Wade McLeod. It had been quick and painless—painless, perhaps, because she had been too numb to feel anything. Not even the brief, hard kiss Wade had planted on her surprised mouth after the short ceremony had made any difference. That might only have been for the sake of appearances—the one thing he was always so insistent about.

She had moved in a kind of dream, she had done ever since Wade had driven her back to Baccaroo, after she had accepted his proposal. He had ordered her not to say anything to anyone, which hadn't been a difficult order to obey, fear if nothing else having kept her lips sealed.

It had, she had thought at the time, been one of the most difficult weeks in her life. The lady visitor who had been indirectly responsible for Wade's engagement had arrived and Vicki had been subject to her charming intolerance—so much so that Vicki had occasionally been tempted almost beyond everything to tell her she was going to marry Wade. She had been forced to run after Miss Barrie hand and foot as the lady had no patience with the aborigine girls. Throughout it all Wade had remained so distant, Vicki decided he must be regretting the whole thing, and for days had alternated between unhappiness and relief. It hadn't been until he had told her, the night before, to be ready to leave for Alice in the morning that she had realised he had meant every word.

The actual ceremony had been brief and they had returned to Baccaroo that same evening. It had all been so easy in the end, but there had been moments Vicki still wanted to forget. Like when old Mr McLeod had found her running downstairs and asked where she was going, dressed up 'like that'. She had only had on a plain little dress in blue, but she had thought she had looked very nice, yet under the Old Man's ruffled stare any self-confidence had faded guiltily and she hadn't been able to think of a thing to say.

It had been left to Wade to tell him curtly that he and Vicki were going to Alice for the day. And the astonishment on the Old Man's face had only been surpassed by the fury which had replaced it, when they had returned and he had discovered the true reason for their trip.

At the last minute, Vicki had suddenly come to her senses. She was attracted to Wade and sure she loved the life out here if nothing else, but what was there going to be in this marriage for Wade? Wouldn't marriage to a girl he had no real feelings for only increase the bitterness which seemed to consume him? It was little use trying to convince herself that because in every other way he was absolutely normal, this feud with his grandfather wasn't a big thing in his life. A wife who had to take second place to this, in a loveless marriage, might soon rue the day she had agreed to it.

She had stopped, pulling urgently on his arm as they had walked quickly down the main street. 'Wade,' she had said breathlessly, as he had halted to look down at her enquiringly, 'there's still time to change your mind. Somehow I'm beginning to wonder if this is such a good idea.'

'It's a bit late, isn't it?' Again, as he had done before leaving Baccaroo, he had surveyed her upraised face intently. 'I don't want to change my mind, but does this mean you've changed yours?'

'No, that is ... I just think ...'

'Come on, then!' His regard, which she had suddenly imagined to be tinged with a reluctant tenderness, had changed grimly. 'You'll get through the day better, Vicki, if you do no more thinking. All you need remember is one word, which I don't think should tax you too much.'

'You mean—yes?'

'Wonderful!' he had exclaimed sarcastically, and she had been glad when Doctor Evans had joined them.

Doctor Evans had been their only witness and even he had looked far from persuaded that he was witnessing a love match. Wade had obviously been in touch with him, but it was at Vicki the doctor had kept glancing, as if something about her pale young face bothered him. He had been kind; in fact Vicki very much doubted if she could have got through the service without him. She had found his kindly presence more reassuring than that of the dark, enigmatic man who became, with a few short sentences, her husband.

After the ceremony the quiet of the afternoon had disintegrated suddenly as news of the wedding had broken out. In spite of all Wade's careful precautions, they had been surrounded by his friends and acquaintances, some of whom confessed frankly that they had flown in specially when they had heard over the radio network. Curiosity as well as smiles had etched their eager faces as they had looked Vicki over, the girl who had captured one of the Territory's most eligible bachelors. If many of them had been rather stunned by Vicki's youth and plain appearance, there had been few who hadn't wished them well.

By direct contrast the row which had followed their immediate return to the station had never faded completely from Vicki's mind. For all she had realised the wrath Wade would incur by marrying a girl like herself, she had found herself terribly dismayed. Mercifully the Old Man hadn't heard over the transceiver, but when Wade had told him he and Vicki were married, she had feared he was about to have a stroke. She had heard of such things happening in the elderly, after a shock, and for a moment, knowing he had done this deliberately, she had hated Wade. It had come to her too late that the Old Man, whatever he had done, could not have deserved this. His face had gone a horrible red and he had choked but, as she had started with alarm and remorse, he had told her he would never acknowledge her as Wade's wife.

It was then that Wade, with his grandfather spluttering and Mrs Clover hovering anxiously in the background, had ordered her to leave them, to go upstairs and wait in his room. Vicki had never known exactly what took place between the two men after that. She hadn't dared ask and Wade never told her, but afterwards, although cold, the Old Man had been civil. She hadn't had to endure the acrimony she had feared, and for this she supposed she had Wade to thank. It was old Mr McLeod's so transparent disappointment which had often almost caused her to break down.

She had expected Wade would want her to continue sleeping in her old room, but in this she found herself mistaken. He had told her at once to fetch her things and put them in his bedroom, that she could use his bed while he would sleep in the adjoining dressing-room. This way no one would realise they were not sleeping together.

Wade had dismissed her anxious enquiries about his grandfather with an indifferent shrug of his broad shoulders. 'He would have liked a big society wedding, to have seen me walking down the aisle with a beautiful, well-known bride. He's disappointed, that's all. But not as much as he's going to be when we don't produce the great-grandchildren he's waiting for.'

Vicki had found it impossible to hide her feelings any longer. Her abhorrence of the situation, her wounded pride and humiliation, had shown on her face. 'In a way, Wade, I'm beginning to think you're just as despicable as he is! I—I feel sorrier for him than you.'

Wade's eyes had glinted, but he had merely given another shrug. 'Calm down, girl. Your sympathy is misplaced. He'll recover, given time.'

Vicki had shuddered. She had stood staring at him, a slightly incongruous figure in her now crumpled blue dress. The sick feeling at the bottom of her stomach told her this was all wrong, but because she had married Wade willingly, for all the wrong reasons, it must be right that she should suffer. Frowning down on her cheap blue dress, she had seen herself instead in a long white bridal gown and veil, on the arm of a smiling, handsome bridegroom. She pictured a reception, an adoring husband by her side—had seen the clouds of confetti, later, as they had started out on their honeymoon. Then the children. Intuitively she had known she could love any number of them, if they belonged to Wade.

Her face flushing, she had turned away, blaming him

silently for the impossible images which had flashed
through her mind. None of these things had happened,
could happen now. Not even the children—as he was to
re-emphasise, in no uncertain terms!

'Keep out of my room, Vicki, out of my life, in everything which matters. You understand?'

Everything might have been a lot different, Vicki thought
miserably, if she had paid a lot more attention to what Wade
had said, if she had tried to obey him strictly to the letter.
For a few weeks she had, she supposed, done as he had
instructed. She had been so unnerved by his continuing
coldness and the Old Man's angry reactions to their marriage, that she had done everything possible to keep out of
their way. Predictable as the pattern of their relationship
had been, she hadn't been completely prepared to cope
with the cold reality. The hurt she sustained she kept to
herself. It was only noticeable in the paleness of her face,
the haunting anxiety in her blue eyes.

She had been surprised, almost disbelieving, when old
Mr McLeod appeared to come round, and the earlier,
cautious friendship between them had begun slowly to
re-establish itself. Once convinced it was actually happening, that the Old Man was really beginning to smile at her
instead of barking, she had thought Wade would be pleased.
But to her dismay she found he was entirely the opposite.

While his grandfather was pleasanter, and gave the impression that he might one day accept her, Wade, on the
other hand, had become gradually grimmer. He had ordered
her to keep out of his room, but appeared to have no com-
punction about entering hers. Sometimes it occurred to
Vicki that he didn't trust her and must keep her under
constant surveillance. Ignoring any need she might feel for
at least friendship between them, the attention he gave her
amounted to nothing less than a kind of indirect imprison-
ment.

When Jeff Curry offered to teach her to ride, Wade had
demurred immediately and taught her himself. He had

gone even further. As if determined to do the job properly he had bought her a beautiful little thoroughbred filly, which Jeff had whispered had cost the earth. In spite of the detached way Wade had handed it over, Vicki had been thrilled to tears with his gift. She had come to love the spirited little horse. Some of the tears she had wept on leaving Baccaroo had been for Firefly.

After the event of Firefly, he had taken to riding out with her occasionally and sometimes even to spending a little longer with her after dinner. Thus encouraged, she had hoped he would approve of his grandfather's partial change of heart and was almost bitterly disappointed that he did not seem to approve at all.

'Don't you see, you little fool,' he had snapped, his face dark with anger as he had paused in her bedroom, on his way to the chest of drawers on the far side of it, 'it might be nothing but a trick. He's just trying to discover exactly what sort of marriage we have.'

# CHAPTER SIX

SOMEHOW Vicki felt lacerated. She had wondered why a few words from Wade, especially those delivered with stony indifference, could make her feel as battered as from heavy blows. 'You mean,' she faltered, her cheeks crimson, as she tried to look at him, 'You mean he would actually like to know if we're sleeping together?'

'You get the general drift.' With a merciless disregard for her embarrassment he had changed course and come to sit on the edge of the bed.

'I don't believe he would actually ask!' she had stammered, staring at him, discomfited.

Wade had returned her stare oppressively, as if he was suddenly more interested in the way she looked than in what she was saying. He frowned as his eyes went over her. She was sitting up in bed in her pyjama jacket, a sheet over her knees, her arms wrapped around them to disguise the fact that she wore no bottoms. The summer was beginning and the night had been hot.

Wade's brows had risen over her warm cheeks. 'You're the one who's being frank, but since you are the answer's yes. Once your friendship's assured he'll get round to it eventually. You don't know my grandfather. He's almost as stubborn as you are. He never gives up.'

'It's probably no great secret, anyway.' Shocked by the bitterness in her voice, she had added quickly, in an attempt to hide it, 'I don't suppose he'd be surprised.'

'No?' Strangely enough this seemed to give Wade food for thought. He had sat regarding her closely for a long moment. Vicki had found herself moving uneasily under his prolonged and calculating stare, but she hadn't been prepared for the disconcerting feeling which had shot through her as his eyes left her face to begin moving slowly over her again, just as they had done a few seconds ago, but his expression changed.

Taking her by surprise, he had leant over her, resting one hand across her as the other went to her head. Lightly he had tugged at a spiky tuft of the fair hair which she always kept so short.

'Why don't you let it grow?' he asked curiously. 'It's thick and soft and a wonderful colour. I think it would suit you to wear it longer.'

She hadn't confessed that she continued keeping it short as, this way, it seemed to constitute a kind of defence. Nothing she properly understood or could explain, but, childishly short like this, her hair might form a barrier, protecting her from feelings which were rapidly growing far from adolescent. Dimly she had begun to realise this, especially when Wade strode, as he often did, shirtless through her bedroom. He might never appear very approachable, but that didn't prevent her being very conscious of him.

The feel of his hand on her head had really been the start of her undoing. Her eyes had clung to him, as if greedy to assimilate every inch of his broad, masculine strength, and the sensible reply she was thinking up had somehow failed to make it.

'Come here!' Quite suddenly, with this short exclamation, he had reached for her, pulling her completely into his arms. When she had gasped in genuine surprise, stiffening instinctively, he had thrust hard fingers around the tenderly curved chin she turned away from him, forcing her back. His movements had been deliberate but unhurried. There was no suggestion that he didn't know exactly what he was doing; it had been as if this was something he had contemplated for a long time, a notion, until now, perhaps unformed at the back of his mind, but he had no intention of spoiling the final moments of anticipation. When, eventually, he had sighed heavily and lowered his mouth to hers, she had known complete devastation.

She had never forgotten, although she liked to believe she had, the first time he had kissed her, when she had bumped into him coming from Miss Morris's room in the middle of the night. Yet this seemed much worse. Crushed against the hard muscles of his chest, she found the masculine scent of his body proved an overpowering stimulant. Within the exquisite cruelty of his grasp every bone in her long, slender limbs had seemed to melt. She had been stunned by the depth of his passion which had wrung a too swift response from her own thudding heart.

Had she tried to resist him? Her heart, even now, beat unevenly when she recalled that scene, and she thought not! In his arms, with his mouth breaking down her defences as he explored hers, there had been everything to entice her, nothing to repulse. He had moulded her to him with his hands and arms and she had been powerless against such physical expertise. It had been like entering an unknown world, seared by sensations she had not known existed. She had only wanted to explore further. Clinging to him shamelessly, she had let the hardness of his demanding mouth deepen on hers until she had stopped thinking and the room began to whirl.

Then she had been freed so quickly she had felt deprived, betrayed. She hadn't been conscious of how she had looked, her skin rose-flushed, her blue eyes heavy with awakening desire, bewildered tears. It had been like being suspended. She had felt as she fancied a star might out in the dazzling galaxy, caught in a scintillating world of the senses before being flung unexpectedly down to earth.

Wade's arms had left her and, as he moved back, she waited numbly for him to get up and walk away. But to her surprise he hadn't. He had remained sitting on her bed but not touching her. When she had brought herself to look at him she had detected something unusual about him—a mixture of satisfaction, a certain cold-blooded excitement. The latter was maybe crazy as she didn't think Wade Mc-

Leod had ever been excited about anything in his life.

What he had said next had shaken her to her very foundations.

'Vicki!' He had made her look at him again, for all she shrank from doing so. He had read in her strained face all the aroused feelings which so confused and frightened her. Feelings, nevertheless, torn by an almost compulsive desire to surrender to them.

'Vicki,' he had repeated, as her breathing had become painfully shallow, 'Doc Evans is calling tomorrow on his way back to Alice. I want you to see him.'

'Doctor Evans?'

'Yes.' Wade's voice had been clipped. From the look in his eyes as they had held hers implacably, she might have been a stranger, but she did notice a definite tension in his jaw. 'God, you're surely old enough to understand without me having to put it into actual words? It appears we might be more vulnerable to human weaknesses than we imagine. And it's no use believing you can leave it all to me. For the first time in my life I'm not sure I can handle everything. You're a very potent combination of innocence and sexuality. You are also, unfortunately, my wife. So— do I have to spell it out? One of these days I might just conceivably lose my sanity and I want to be sure there are no repercussions. Do you follow?'

All that night Vicki had fretted. She would have had to be very dim indeed not to have realised that Wade had been referring to the family he didn't want. The one he refused to have, no matter what his wife's feelings. And she was his wife, Vicki thought hollowly, despite the fact that this was the first time he had kissed her since they were married.

Vaguely she understood the dangers he had mentioned regarding their feelings, aware, for the first time, how easily they could get out of hand. Especially when she loved him. Like a bolt from the blue she had suddenly become conscious of this. It caused shock waves to sweep her again and again. Love wasn't a thing she had given much thought to, although she remembered feeling guilty about it, when she had first agreed to marry Wade. But she hadn't really believed such a thing existed. Now that the actuality of it hit her, she felt horrified. There was none of the pleasure which such an emotion must usually bring; only a harsh hurt because Wade would never love her. She recalled his detached tones, which had reduced any attraction between them down to frightening, harsh basics. She had known what he was about. He didn't want children and was taking no risks, but it was the totally unemotional way he alluded to it that tormented her terribly. It could only happen by accident. Never intentionally would he come near her. He had never intended kissing her that night; it had been one of those things which just happened.

Vicki, in spite of her apprehension, had rebelled. She remembered being determined, that night, that she would never see Doctor Evans. Never would she ask him for help she didn't intend making use of.

How she had found herself in the study alone with Doctor Evans next day, she never knew. She had felt horribly embarrassed as the door had closed softly behind Wade and furious that, for all her resolutions, he seemed to have outwitted her. He also seemed to have explained to the doctor exactly what she wanted, as he hadn't kept her long. Frank Evans couldn't have been nicer, or more diplomatic, but all the same she had hated it!

She had felt trapped after that, caught between her resolve to keep Wade at a distance and her love for him—a love which brought an increasing desire to be in his arms again. Yet he had never attempted to so much as touch her for a very long time, and when he did she was sure it hadn't been premeditated. Afterwards she had thought perhaps he had been trying as hard as she to see that nothing happened to disturb the emotions which seemed to have settled down, if uneasily.

Jeff had cut his hand, his right hand, and the cut had been deep. Mrs Clover hadn't been well and had gone early to bed; the Old Man, too, had retired. There hadn't been anyone else around and, rather than waste time looking for someone, Vicki had gone to the office herself, and got the nurse on the transceiver which was connected to the Flying Doctor radio network in Alice Springs.

The Royal Flying Doctor Service began early each morning with a doctor and nurse sitting in front of a microphone giving medical advice to people in the Outback who came on the air and described their symptoms. When someone was too ill for treatment a nurse or a doctor would fly out to the cattle station or perhaps an aborigine settlement and fly the patient back to the hospital in Alice Springs. The radio network was also used to organise the routine trips during which clinics were held in the various settlements and smaller towns.

Vicki, nervous because she wasn't yet entirely used to it, had been relieved to find her call went without a hitch. She carried out the nurse's instructions on a sickly-looking Jeff successfully. Afterwards, because he had still appeared dazed, she had walked with him to his bungalow and got him a drink. She had waited until he had recovered sufficiently to get himself to bed, and had just been leaving when Wade found her.

Wade had been to Sydney on business but had declined to take Vicki. She hadn't decided whether or not she had wanted to go but had felt hurt because he hadn't asked. He had just flown in from Alice and suspicion had flared with what she had thought unreasonable anger in his eyes.

'Why, you little tramp!' he had exclaimed brutally, coming to a sudden halt in front of her, his voice like steel. 'Can't I leave you for a few days without this? This, I presume, is why you wouldn't come with me?'

He must have forgotten he had never invited her. Although feeling angrily indignant she had tried to keep calm, warning herself that Wade must be tired, not really aware of the terse insults he hurled at her. Steadying herself, she had begun telling him about Jeff's hand, but he hadn't listened.

Curtly he had cut her off before she could even get started. 'I've seen the way Jeff looks at you.'

'Well, I haven't!' Instinctively she had tried to appease him, although she didn't perhaps frame her words wisely or get quite the right inflection in her voice. Maybe the resentment inside her had been too strong and she had been too tired. What with one thing and another it had been quite a day. 'You're letting your imagination run away with you, Wade. I was anxious about Jeff because ...'

'I know why you were worried,' he had broken in sarcastically. 'Don't all women pretend to worry when they know a man's fallen for them? They worry that the poor devil might feel hurt, when they've done their damnedest to see that he is. You're probably ready to weep tears of anguish over Jeff, but I don't have to listen. I don't want to hear you mention Jeff Curry again.'

'Oh—but Wade,' her blue eyes, rounding with distress, had given the very impression she sought to avoid, 'you don't understand!'

'Be quiet!'

The tightness to his mouth stunned her. His scorn began hitting her in waves and she had flinched. 'I must ...'

Again, as she tried to mention Jeff's hand, he choked her off. 'Vicki! Will you please shut up and get out of my sight, before we both say things we might be sorry for.'

Reduced to an unwilling silence by the sheer force of his strong personality, Vicki had stared up at him. If he was happy to believe the worst of her why should she tear herself apart trying to enlighten him as to what had really happened? Wade, at his best, was inclined to be sceptical about most things and, in the mood he was in this evening, it didn't seem likely he would trust anything she said. In the morning, though, he would have to face the facts he refused to listen to. Vicki dwelt sullenly on the apology

he would be forced to make. However repentant he might
be it would be a long time before she forgave him!

With a contemptuous lift of her chin, which was to prove
her undoing, she had turned from him to run into the
house. She was aware that he stalked furiously behind her,
but as his anger was usually controlled, she hadn't felt
unusually frightened. She would go straight to bed. If he
wanted something to eat he could get it himself! Along
with everything else, she didn't have to put up with his
bad temper.

Hurrying upstairs, she had had a quick shower and tumbled into bed in a flash, not even stopping to run a comb
through her still damp hair. Her heart felt sore with a
weight of wounded feelings. She loved Wade, yet all he
ever did was abuse her. He didn't seem to think she was
capable of anything, least of all integrity! With a small sob
she groped for the switch, and turned off the light. Another day gone, she remembered sighing, little dreaming
this one was far from over, and that the end of it would be
much more devastating than the beginning.

She had heard Wade in the bathroom, the faint noise of
the shower. The slight silence, then doors closing, hers
opening.

She had kept her eyes tight shut, pretending to be asleep.
He had been out and in a lot lately, always looking for
something, seeing if she wanted anything before wishing
her a cool goodnight. But, after the way he had just spoken
to her outside, she hadn't thought he would have the nerve
to come near her. Quietly she turned her back on him, hud-
dling beneath the sheets.

When the same sheets had suddenly been ripped off her
she had been shocked, frightened almost out of her wits.
'Wade!' Her eyes, after that first paralysed moment, shooting wide open, she had made a frantic attempt to grab
something—anything, to cover herself with. 'How dare
you!' she had cried, fright giving strength to her trembling
voice, as he had towered above her, surveying her near

nakedness with cold, stony eyes.

'I thought as much,' his mouth had curled as she had struggled frantically to wrap herself in a blanket. 'Does Jeff know you sleep with next to nothing on?'

She had been kneeling, almost upright, on the bed, very near to him. It had merely taken the lifting of one tightly clenched fist to hit him across his coldly insulting face.

Unfortunately it was also all it took to remove the curb on his explosive anger. With a half bitten off curse, as Vicki's hand contacted his cheek, he grabbed hold of her. The protective blanket had fallen from her numb fingers as he had hauled her savagely to him, uncaring if he hurt.

She had fought him, even before she had been fully aware of his intentions. His arm had been like an iron band around her and the expression on his face devoid of any tenderness. He was holding her tightly against him as if enjoying the way in which she trembled in the cruel grip of his hands.

'Stop struggling,' he had commanded grimly. 'It's time you learnt I don't appreciate being slapped. Perhaps it's also time you learnt to be a real wife instead of only pretending to be one.'

She had tried to stop him. She wanted to belong to him, but not like this. If he intended taking her in anger there could surely be no joy in it for either of them. If there was any pleasure to be derived from this sort of thing? Somehow, for the moment, in her innocence, she had doubted it.

Apprehension seared through her as he relentlessly set about removing her pyjama jacket and, as her hand came free, she hit out at him again, regardless of his warning. She had been determined to fight him—until he had started kissing her. That, for Vicki, had been the beginning of her final capitulation.

That was when cold logic had flown out of the window and panic had given way to less reasonable instincts. As his mouth possessed hers every nerve in her body had seemed to stop beating. As his free hand had closed over the gentle curve of her slight breast her desire to fight him snuffed out, as a flame might between two fingers.

His mouth had made sure of her utter subjugation, even as he had raised it to mutter harshly, 'I don't intend Jeff Curry to have what I paid for.'

'He never has!' Her struggle for breath had robbed that of the emphasis she had tried to give it, and he had laughed derisively.

'Nor do I intend being the joke of the Territory!' he had added thickly, his hands already exploring parts of her body no one had ever touched before.

Almost begging him to listen, she had whispered hoarsely, 'You're mistaken, Wade! Please don't do anything you might regret. Oh, darling, please stop!'

But he had not. For a moment, as he had drawn back, she thought he had, but it had only been to shrug himself out of his bathrobe. She had flinched to feel his skin, bare against hers, but her revulsion had been short- lasting. As his mouth came against her throat and his hands aroused her to a pitch of feverish excitement she had felt her own arms going out, clinging to him, with the wild insanity of someone on the point of drowning.

Then his mouth had returned to hers and she had turned frightened again, in spite of the flames consuming her body, as she had felt the force of his rising passion. But he hadn't allowed her breath to give voice to her rising fears, nor taken any notice when he must have sensed her virginal nervousness. It seemed he was only prepared to acknowledge the sensuous response which she hadn't the experience to hide, which was an innate part of her.

She had heard his smothered exclamation and felt the roughness of his heated flesh, and betraying shivers had gone down her spine. His mouth had closed over hers and driven by his strong passion he had taken her. He hadn't listened to her cries of protest or seemed to notice the tears on her small face.

Bitterly, when it was all over, she had sobbed, perhaps more from disappointment than from hurt. If he had used tenderness, a little patience, how different it might have been, but with anger and intolerance driving him it would have been too much to hope for. Her immediate reactions had been too mixed and confused to understand properly, but she remembered feeling tearfully resentful that, while Wade had appeared savagely satisfied, she had felt somehow cheated.

It hadn't helped that he had left her almost immediately. Subconsciously, she realised now, she must have been hoping he would stay. In spite of the way he had made her suffer, she knew she had been hoping vaguely for something else. Something which she had groped for, striven desperately after, might have achieved if the time in his arms had been just a little longer. What it was she had not found out—not then!

Next morning, to her surprise, he had entered her room, with a ruthlessness that reminded her of something else. She had been attempting to brush her short hair before going downstairs and had been startled as he usually went out early. Seeing him standing behind her, she had stiffened, the brush in her hand falling with a small clatter on to the dressing table from which she had just picked it up. After a quick glance she hadn't been able to look at him, not after a sleepless night, during which strangely erotic dreams had faded before stronger elements of shame and anger.

Apparently Wade was no keener to look at her. His voice had been curt to the point of indifference. He didn't greet her formally or otherwise. He had every appearance of a man with something to say and a need to have it done with as soon as possible. 'I've just learnt about Jeff's hand.'

'Oh, I see ...' Keeping her eyes averted, she had hastily stuck her hands into the back pockets of her jeans, to hide their agitated trembling. She hadn't noticed how his gaze had narrowed on her white face, the tear-reddened eyes, he could see through the glass.

'I'm sorry for what happened last night,' he had said, neither his eyes or voice expressing the remorse he pretended. 'I'm sorry, if only because it made me realise that at least one of my accusations was unjust.'

Lowering her head still further, she had whispered, 'You mean you're ready to admit I've not been a tramp?'

'Vicki!' As if suffering from a kind of unsolvable frustration, he had exclaimed grimly, 'I have apologised. I'll acknowledge frankly I was mistaken. I'm sorry I was so rough. It was too late when I realised. All the other women I've known have been experienced.'

'All of them?' she had whispered, the pain of hearing him admitting his previous affairs almost worse than the physical one she had known through the night.

'Sure,' his voice had hardened, as if deliberately. 'Most of my life has been dedicated to work, Vicki, but I've been no saint. Nor have I ever pretended to be. But you were immaculate, my dear, and don't have to worry about things like that. As for some girls being tramps, if they are, I guess it's only what men have made them.'

'Yes,' she had whispered stupidly, wanting only to be in his arms again.

'Good,' he had returned, tautly. 'I'm glad you understand.' Then swinging on his heel, after another stony glance at her desolate face, he had left her, as if the few brief words he had spared her were all that was necessary.

The next few weeks had passed terribly slowly, a succession of days to be got through somehow. Days which had seemed to leave her either devoid of feeling or filled with an agony of frustrated longing. Helping Mrs Clover had proved no answer, although Mrs Clover was always nice to her. Daily the housekeeper had appeared to grow more pleased that Vicki and Wade had got married, though she still shook her head over the way Wade had done it. Helping Wade's now very friendly grandfather wasn't much good either. Being tired to the point of exhaustion didn't seem to make much difference to some things!

Loving Wade, yet not knowing how best to approach him, had worn her almost to a shadow. Since that night in her room he had mostly ignored her and she couldn't seem to find a way through the barrier he had erected between them. Any attempts she had made to improve matters had met with failure. The one time she had actually managed to get near him had merely been turned into something he had used against her later.

The one time she had really let him see she wouldn't mind being a proper wife to him, they had been coming upstairs together, late one night. Accidentally she had stumbled against him, and automatically he had caught her, momentarily holding her to him. After she had steadied herself, instead of leaving him, she had found her arms creeping around his neck.

'Wade?' Her young face full of unconscious but naked longing, she had whispered his name, and suddenly he had bent his tall head and kissed her.

'Oh, Wade——' as his mouth had lifted, she'd hung on to him tightly, her eyes warm with love, 'Wade,' she had whispered breathlessly, 'couldn't we——?'

His glance had darkened, as it had gone swiftly over her. His eyes had been slightly puzzled, as if he had found her different, without being able to put his finger on it. Then he had let her go abruptly.

'Go to bed,' he had said tautly, his face so hard he didn't have to add, 'alone.' 'This was never part of our agreement and I don't intend drawing up a new one, even for the future. As for these little animal instincts of yours, I'd advise you to grow up before you offer yourself again to anyone. Until you know exactly what you might be starting!'

'But, Wade——' She hadn't understood much of what he was saying, her senses had been clamouring so she could think of only one thing. She had felt shame, but this had been swiftly smothered by her inner turbulence.

He hadn't, however, been sympathetic. 'I don't want to

ever call you a tramp again, Vicki, but you're certainly asking for it. Try learning to control yourself.'

At that she had pulled herself from his arms, his message getting clearly through to her at last, her eyes wide with the force of her emotions. There had also been resentment, a painful realisation that he had no time for her, and nothing she had said or done had given him any cause to change his mind regarding his original plan for their marriage.

It had been just after this that she had realised something which had completely stunned her. She had begun feeling ill, particularly in the mornings. And when she had got down to really thinking about it, she had known that certain physical changes could only be caused through one thing. For a long time she had refused to believe it could have happened to her—until the morning Wade had found her in the bathroom.

It had been after eight and he had been gone for hours. He must have come back for something. He caught her being sick.

'Vicki?' she had scarcely heard his surprised exclamation, she had been so ill. 'What the devil is the matter with you, girl?'

'Oh, please go away!' she had moaned, sobbing in her distress, making an abortive attempt to get rid of him. Fear of possible reprisals, should he guess, sharpened her dulled wits, enabling her to gasp quickly, 'It must be something I ate for dinner last night.'

'Dinner?' His brows had gathered, as he had watched her rinsing her coldly perspiring face. He had grasped her shoulders, swinging her around to him.

Water had dripped down her thin shirt as his eyes had gone narrowly over her, in much the same way as they had done on that last terrible evening on the stairs. Now, as they rested on the new, rounded fullness of her figure, the blue shadows under eyes set in a white, smudged face, realisation merged with a terrible anger.

'Why, you little cheat!' He hadn't minced his words.

He had looked as if he would have liked to hit her. His tall, lean body had been rigid. 'How long have you been like—this?'

'Not long.' Not having been able to meet fury with fury, she had shrunk from the terrible suspicion in his eyes. Her heavy lashes had fallen unhappily, guilt and misery preventing her from even trying to defend herself.

His hands had been cruel on her shaking shoulders as he had forced her to look at him. 'How can it be? You saw Doc Evans—he told me you'd had a satisfactory chat. Did you, in God's name, follow his advice?'

'No ...' Even shaking with nerves, she had known it would be useless to lie to him. She had shaken her head and, like an idiot, kept on shaking it until he had ordered her to stop. 'No,' she repeated dully, 'I never took any of what he gave me.'

'Why not?' The unrelenting harshness of his voice seemed to cause her actual pain. 'Didn't I specifically ask you to because of what might happen? What did happen, as you very well know. I trusted you to keep your side of the bargain.'

In vain she had searched for one sign of tenderness in him. 'I'm sorry,' she quivered, 'I just didn't think there'd be any need.' While this was true, it would have been more honest to confess how she had disliked the idea of doing anything to avoid having Wade's child.

'You little fool!' His eyes had smouldered and she had cringed, afraid suddenly of what he might do to her. That he wanted to inflict some kind of punishment had been so obvious she was terrified. His grey eyes had stared straight into hers and there had been no pity in him anywhere.

'I don't know if you thought you could deceive me and get away with it,' he had said savagely, 'but if you did then you'd better think again! You can pack your bags and get out of here, just as quick as you like!'

'Wade!' she had gasped, tears of terror and anguish falling uncontrollably down her cheeks as she had clutched at his shirt with hysterical hands. 'You can't mean it! How could I go anywhere? I haven't anywhere to go to, and if I had, how could I get there?'

'Any way you like!' Fury sweeping him, he had thrown her off. 'I'm just leaving with Jeff to inspect some stock I'm interested in, in Queensland. I'll be away a couple of days. When I come back I want you gone, out of my sight, and I don't want to see you again. Get one of the men to take you into Alice. From there you can easily return to the U.K.'

'I'll do that.' Scarcely realising what she was saying, she had nodded blindly.

With a small exclamation of pain, which was still too vivid, seeing that all this had happened over four years ago, Vicki sat up sharply, clutching her head. Why did she still remember it so torturously? She had fainted when Wade had left her, and Mrs Clover had found her lying on the floor and made a great fuss. Thankfully, Vicki had seen how Mrs Clover had believed her story of being a little run down. Just as she had been relieved when Mrs Clover had agreed that a trip to Alice would make a nice change and that she could get a tonic while she was there.

Vicki hadn't packed a bag, so as to arouse no suspicion. She had simply put on her hat and flown, and no one had been any the wiser. Mrs Clover had suspected nothing.

Vicki sighed, dwelling briefly but sorrowfully on all that had happened since, including the news which made her heart ache with regret. Mrs Clover had died and she hadn't known. The housekeeper had been a friend, especially when she had needed one, and she had never really thanked her properly. Vicki wished, now, that she had written. She had wanted to, but had always been so scared that Wade might conceivably learn where she was living even if she put no address. In a granny-like fashion, Mrs Clover would have been so pleased with Graham, and Vicki knew she would have appreciated the older woman's advice. Her mouth twisting wryly, she stared through the small piece of visible window, tears of deep unhappiness in her eyes for what might have been, if only her marriage had been a normal one.

During the next few days her strength returned quite quickly.

'So it should, at your age!' Miss Webb, with her superior ten years, informed Vicki tartly, adding, with more condescension than Vicki thought her position allowed, 'I must say the house runs more smoothly since you've got back on your feet again. I told your husband there was no need to worry, that all you needed was a little extra rest.'

Vicki smiled faintly, refusing to be impressed by that. She could have retorted sharply, but Miss Webb was curious enough without giving her more to think about. Her growing tendency to introduce Wade into every other sentence was becoming a regrettable if unintentional habit. She wondered if Wade encouraged her in this, then decided not. Miss Webb was disposed to be friendly towards anyone who would talk to her. No—Vicki frowned ruefully, as Miss Webb rambled on; Miss Webb only wanted someone prepared to listen to her endless monologues about her own clever achievements and brilliant relations. Miss Webb, Vicki realised dispiritedly, was a wonderful children's nurse, and her absorption in her personal affairs was probably all to the good. She never appeared to overlook a thing. But unfortunately her curiosity regarding the situation at Baccaroo was beginning to get the better of her. Any day now, Vicki suspected, Miss Webb was going to throw discretion to the winds and risk asking Vicki why this was the first time Graham had been at Baccaroo. Where previously she had hinted she would begin asking outright.

From there it would be only be a short step to wondering why Graham hadn't known his father, and the answer to that might find Miss Webb speculating accurately on Vicki's exact relationship with her husband. There might be no end to it, Vicki thought doubtfully, if she didn't learn to manage Miss Webb properly.

If only she had some proper status! Then she could

have put Miss Webb firmly in her place—at least, so there would be no more personal questions! As things stood she guessed that if Miss Webb were to find out even half of the truth, her life might be a misery.

As she daily grew stronger, Vicki resolved to ask Wade if Miss Webb couldn't be done without. It wouldn't be unkind as Miss Webb was constantly complaining of the isolation. She was also forever proclaiming that she could pick and choose when it came to jobs, that she had only agreed to come here because it was a feather in her cap to be working for the McLeods. As things stood, Vicki was never sure when Miss Webb was going to gather sufficient courage to bring up the subject of Wade and herself, and strangely apprehensive of this, her nerves grew taut.

# CHAPTER SEVEN

VICKI realised she must catch Wade in a good mood, which wouldn't be easy. For one thing, his relationship with his son was becoming increasingly difficult. Try as she might to keep them apart, there seemed to be almost daily clashes. Graham, having apparently inherited much of Wade's grim determination, usually made a beeline for his father whenever he saw him—something which neither Vicki or Miss Webb were often quick enough to prevent.

Vicki found herself torn, as usual, between misery and regret as she watched them together. Half the trouble, she was ready to admit, was her own feelings of what could only amount to jealousy, when it became quite obvious that Graham was ready to worship his newly acquired father—to such an extent that his mother, equally obviously, was beginning to take second place. Third place, perhaps, Vicki thought bitterly, seeing how Miss Webb took up most of his day.

She wouldn't have minded so much as it was only for a short time, and with the full responsibility of her small son removed from her shoulders she would have been less than honest to deny that it made no difference. For all her love for Graham hadn't changed, she found her new freedom surprisingly welcome. It might have been more appreciated if it hadn't had to be set against a future which might only be made more difficult because of it. Graham, being so young, might forget more easily than she would.

One discovery, after her return, was to give her some moments of great joy, a joy which was to alleviate a little of the black depression that haunted her. She was out looking for Graham and Miss Webb one afternoon. Having got ahead with preparations for dinner, she gave in to the temptation to take a walk. So far, since she had come back, she had kept almost entirely to the house, reluctant to explore those places she had learnt to love and must leave again. When Graham chatted to her about the creek and the stockyards, the horses and all the men, she made no comment, gave no indication that her heart might be aching.

This afternoon, however, she hadn't been able to resist coming out. Slipping into a pair of jeans and thin top, she let her long, fine hair blow free and ran down to the paddocks. The sun was still hot, but not as hot as it had been immediately after lunch. It would only grow warmer as the Australian summer progressed. Everywhere was quiet, she felt she had the whole place to herself. Wade was out with some contractors, putting down a bore on one of the far reaches of the station, where the land was scarcely more than barren desert. She had heard him fly out. It could be hours before he was home again.

It was in this strangely lighter mood, as she ran with flying footsteps over the burnt up grass towards the creek where she hoped to find Graham, that she came across Firefly. At first she couldn't believe it. Without realising what she was doing, she halted abruptly, leaning over the picket fence towards the peacefully grazing horse at the other side of the paddock. Firefly had been a beautiful little filly, not as powerful as some of Wade's big Arabians but a thoroughbred for all that, through and through. Inexperienced in the ways of horses until she had come here, Vicki had learnt fast, but Firefly, while being able to live up to her name, had never put a foot wrong.

Vicki, after the first terrible seconds of heart-stopping contemplation, knew beyond all doubt that it was the same little horse Wade had given her. Suddenly, impulsively, she called its name, her pure, clear voice ringing over the space between them. 'Firefly!'

The horse reared, lifting its head as it whirled, with a graceful elegance of shining mane and dancing hooves. Then it halted, as Vicki called again, this time her voice warm with excitement. Responding, Firefly tossed her head some more, whinnying as she trotted curiously towards the girl who was running to meet her.

Recklessly Vicki threw her arms around the prancing mare's neck, tears tumbling down her cheeks as she realised Firefly loved and recognised her. Joyfully she hugged the little horse while Firefly nudged her again and again.

'She remembers you, Vicki. I'm glad.'

Startled, Vicki turned. It was Jeff Curry. Her face flushed with happiness and damp with tears, she stammered, 'I never thought Firefly would still be here.'

'I don't suppose you did. She missed you, Vicki.' Jeff's smile faded bleakly. 'We all did. Vicki—I——'

Vicki broke in hurriedly, sensing danger, if not quite sure where it lay. Glancing away from Jeff's taut face, she said quickly, 'I thought Wade would have sold her.'

'He wouldn't part with her.' Jeff appeared to take hold of himself. 'Nor would he ever allow anyone to ride her, after you went.'

She drew a swift breath, aware that he was watching her closely. 'I—I suppose he had his reasons.' Tears still clinging to her long lashes, she rubbed her cheek adoringly against the horse.

Then Wade was there, appearing from nowhere, staring grimly at the tender hand Jeff had laid on her arm. As she shook it anxiously off Wade came closer, his eyes remaining on Vicki as she stood, slim and straight, between them.

'I never dreamt,' she swallowed nervously when he didn't speak, 'you would keep Firefly. I'm—I'm grateful.'

It must have been the wrong thing to say before Jeff, as she saw anger flash through Wade's watchful eyes.

As Wade's mouth hardened, Jeff excused himself, 'I'll see you later.' He must have been speaking to Wade, but it was at Vicki he looked.

As soon as he was gone Wade turned on her curtly. 'Do you have to make remarks like that in front of Jeff? Why shouldn't I have kept the horse? She's from good stock.'

'Otherwise,' Vicki spoke bitterly, 'you'd have let her go?'

'Maybe.'

'Wade McLeod,' she whispered fiercely, 'please don't make me hate you more than I do!'

His smile was mirthless, his eyes suddenly calculating as they rested on her slender figure. His gaze wandered slowly, almost insultingly so, over her long blonde hair, down to her long legs, then back up to where her breasts curved, frankly seductive, under her thin body shirt. 'It seems you think I shouldn't object when I find my wife holding hands with my foreman! Maybe,' he added softly, 'you won't mind if I take a few liberties? I could give you something to really hate me for before you leave. I remember you weren't always quite so eager to dislike me!'

A spark of something unreadable flickered quickly through Vicki, before she suddenly clutched at her pride. Firefly nudged her and she turned her face to the horse again, not wanting to remember how she had once felt about Wade, nor how that night she had spent in his arms had never ceased to haunt her. It had made such an impression she had never been able to look at another man. How often, when telling herself she couldn't, because of Graham, she had known he was not the real reason. Now Wade was older, looked definitely older as he stood looking down on her so coldly. So, come to think of it, was she, but nothing seemed to have changed.

Making an effort to steer clear of what she felt instinctively to be dangerous ground, she said, 'A lot of time has passed since then. Anyway, I'm very happy to see Firefly again. Graham loves the pony your grandfather gave him. Perhaps we can go riding together.'

'Perhaps.'

'Graham's coming on quite well.'

'I believe.'

An underlying sharpness edged his voice and her eyes flashed. 'Do you always use such an economy of words?'

'As regards your son, you mean?' he drawled sarcastically.

She wanted to scream, 'He's yours as well, isn't he?' but the contempt in his face deterred her. 'If you like,' she agreed frigidly.

'No, I don't like!' His low exclamation of anger alarmed her, as his hands came out to pull her suddenly away from the horse. 'There's a lot of things I don't like about this whole situation, but much that I'm forced to put up with.'

'Don't worry,' her breathing quickened almost audibly when he didn't let her go, 'you'll soon be free to marry again. Very soon, I should imagine, if your grandfather has many more attacks like his last. Or you might simply prefer to lead the bachelor existence you've grown so fond of!'

'And you?' he bit out harshly, a vicious look on his face. 'You don't have to pretend you won't enjoy your freedom! You won't have to look guilty when a man like Jeff looks you over and holds your hand.'

She glared at him. 'No, I won't, will I?' she jeered.

'Why, you little——'

'Don't say it!' she cried sharply, feeling wildly she might lose all control if he called her a tramp. That brought back memories she still couldn't bear to think about.

'Perhaps the time for saying things is past.' There was a savage ruthlessness in his expression as he twisted her nearer. Then his arms were around her, his lips covering hers, crushing them with the hard warmth she recalled so vividly. For a moment she resisted, fighting the rising, hungry urgency in her body, as the whole of her was caught up in emotional turmoil. Before she realised what she was doing she had entwined her arms around his neck, as if urging him to hold her closer.

One of his arms was about her waist while the other went around her back, his hands moulding her to him. He seemed to take a cruel pleasure in letting her feel the full strength of his hard muscles.

Then Graham was calling from the other side of the paddock, his small, shrill voice bringing Vicki sharply back to earth. As Wade slowly lifted his head she flushed scarlet and dragged her arms from his neck. The speculation in his eyes as she did so told her better than words that he was well aware where they had been.

'Your son, madam!' his voice mocked. 'He still makes a habit of turning up when he isn't wanted.'

'I wanted him!' There had always been moments in Vicki's life when she found herself uttering the last thing she intended. This was one of them, as she knew she and Wade were thinking of exactly the same thing. The flush on her face deepened uncomfortably and she was glad Graham reached them before Wade could jeer at her remark.

Wade's tall body must have disguised the fact that she was with him. Halting a short step ahead of Miss Webb, Graham blinked at her, before looking up at his father. 'Nurth Webb and I've been down by the creek.'

'Fine,' Wade smiled at Miss Webb, who for once was depriving him of more than his share of her attention as her gaze rested on Vicki's hot cheeks.

Wade's eyes glinted as he read the startled surprise in the nurse's face. He spoke to Graham. 'Your mother and I have just been looking over her horse. When she's stronger you can take her out riding. Miss Webb, too, of course.'

As Graham almost visibly grew ten feet taller, Vicki wondered hollowly how Wade, while hating being a father, always managed to say the right thing. How was she going to tear Graham from the station when the time came? Clearly he adored Wade, for all he received little encouragement.

They turned towards the house. As they moved, Wade's hand came under Vicki's elbow, but the hard dig of his fingers warned her this was no friendly gesture, no silent apology for his rough caresses of a moment ago.

Under cover of Graham's excited chatter, he said softly,

'I'll get one of the boys to ride Firefly out a bit. She should be ready for you next week.'

'That won't be necessary, surely?'

'She hasn't been ridden for a long time.' His voice, only loud enough for her ears, seemed to be telling her something. 'Not since you were last at Baccaroo.'

'I see.' She wasn't altogether sure she did, but had no intention of asking a lot of questions. The more detached she kept herself the easier it would be in the long run. It must be sufficient, right now, that Firefly was still here. Adoringly she patted the horse goodbye, as they left the paddock.

The men were coming in from their day's work, some riding, others in jeeps and Landrovers, open trucks. Horses were not used nearly as much as they used to be on cattle stations in the Outback, she heard Wade telling Graham. A lot of horses were even turned loose and ran wild. Some of the wild stallions could occasionally be dangerous, and these Graham must learn to look out for, especially when he was out with his mother.

Listening with half an ear, Vicki watched the returning crew warily. Some she recognised, but there were new faces which she didn't. Whether familiar or not, she soon realised they were mostly staring at her curiously, and nervously she tried to wriggle from Wade's side, muttering an excuse about having to see to dinner.

To her dismay and surprise, Wade objected. 'Don't you want to see Graham's pony?'

'I—well, I'm not sure.'

'Mummy!' Graham's small face was suddenly eager. 'Please!' He tugged her hand. 'You've never ever seen him.'

'Well,' weakly Vicki gave in, 'I suppose I could.' Yet she had no desire to expose herself to the speculation in dozens of pairs of eyes, which she knew might be a possibility if she walked the length of the complex with Wade and Graham. 'It was only dinner,' she continued protesting apprehensively. 'I should really get it started.'

'Perhaps Miss Webb will see to it, for a few minutes.'
With a smile meant to charm, Wade glanced at the nurse,
'I'm sure just a word of advice to the girls will be all that's
necessary, until Graham's mother returns.'

'Oh yes, of course, Mr McLeod!' Miss Webb was full
of words of advice—he couldn't have put it more aptly.

'Did you have to get rid of her?' Vicki whispered
fiercely, her heart aching that he hadn't called her his wife.
She forgot she had been pondering on ways and means of
getting rid of Miss Webb permanently.

'Not really,' he replied, still retaining his hold on her
arm, although not so tightly. 'I just thought it might be a
good idea to let everyone see me with my family. I'm
tired of finding members of my crew loitering around the
house, trying to catch a glimpse of you.'

'Maybe it's understandable,' she muttered unhappily.

'Very,' he agreed dryly.

Vicki swallowed. 'But what sense can be in it?' she exclaimed. 'I'll soon be gone. They'll be even more curious
then.'

'That will be my problem, not yours.'

'Yes, I realise.' Her face went white. 'I didn't think.'

It didn't take long to inspect Graham's pony. At least,
it mightn't have done if he hadn't insisted on demonstrating
how well he could ride. Vicki was forced to watch as Wade,
with a mysterious tolerance, helped him saddle up. After
this, she and Wade stood, she supposed like a pair of fond
parents, admiring Graham's amazing prowess around one
of the stock yards. He had the appearance of a boy who had
ridden for years, not weeks.

The longest moments were those during which Vicki met
several of the station staff, among the crowd which suddenly materialised as if from nowhere to watch Graham.
Contrarily, as she listened to Wade introducing her as 'my
wife,' she wondered why he bothered. There seemed no
sense in going to such lengths for such a short time and

she could quite easily have kept out of sight in the house.

Dinner that evening was better than usual, perhaps because Vicki forced herself to concentrate on it to the exclusion of everything else. In no way did she allow herself to dwell on the non-domestic events of the afternoon. The iced soup she made was perfection and the fruit tart she baked to follow the main course was really something—if a fruit tart could be described this way. When Wade praised it, however, Miss Webb cleverly took the whole of the credit, her eyes so wide and starry she positively glowed.

A cold feeling inside her, Vicki noticed Wade's idle glance concentrate on the nurse's triumphant face. She saw his eyes linger with a hint of interested speculation and something in her stomach churned. It wasn't until she looked away that she realised old Mr McLeod had also caught that exchange of looks and was sharply suspicious. Maybe she could leave Miss Webb to the old man. If Vicki hadn't ever been good enough for his grandson, it went without saying Miss Webb never would be. And he would certainly be taking no more risks. Vicki was very rarely spiteful, but she felt in this instance, as Miss Webb positively simpered over the table at Wade, that she might be excused.

Yet none of this seemed to solve anything as far as Graham was concerned. Later Vicki realised this and the whole problem of Miss Webb continued to bother her. It had been crazy to imagine she could leave her to the Old Man. Wade would never take any notice of him.

It was, Vicki decided wearily, up to her to fight her own battles. Today, Wade's attitude towards Graham had appeared to be softening, but frightened her almost more than his cold indifference had done. She wouldn't have believed it, but it did. What, when his grandfather died, if he decided to keep Graham and get rid of her? There would be little point in denying his own son, after the old man went. Graham would be no trouble, especially with a nurse already installed.

So upset did she feel, she was unable to rest. Her room was clean but still Spartan; there was no soothing, comforting atmosphere to induce sleep. Wade, after he had seen how she had half killed herself scrubbing the dressing room out, had been slightly kinder, but nothing else had changed. She still used the hard little bed and her feet trod the bare lino.

Once she had got used to it, Vicki found this didn't worry her unduly. Tonight she didn't think of it at all. Wade was going off early in the morning. After dinner he had disappeared. Misilgoe had told her he had gone to see Jeff, in his bungalow, and Vicki wondered how much longer it would be before he came in. It seemed suddenly imperative that she see him about Miss Webb right away.

At last she heard sounds of him moving next door. He had not been in the bathroom, but sometimes he used the one along the corridor. Her face pale but set with determination, she tapped on the communicating door. It would have served him right, she thought, with false bravado, if she had just gone straight in!

There was a long silence, during which she wondered if she had been mistaken, then he called for her to come in. He was there, after all. He was not in bed and his brows lifted in dry surprise as she opened the door and walked through it, though he must have guessed who was there.

'The last person on earth,' he jeered harshly, 'I expected to see here!'

'I'm sorry,' she said carefully, not looking at him too directly. 'I had to see you, but I don't want to stay. If you would come to my room for a few minutes, I'd be grateful.'

'The bed's too small, for one thing.' His mouth twisted caustically, as if he wasn't too impressed by his own wit. 'What's wrong with this?' he asked curtly.

'Why, nothing.' She did look at him squarely this time. 'It's just that you ordered me not to come here again.'

'Dear me!' he grinned, completely without mirth. 'You don't mean to tell me that's what's been stopping you?'

Vicki glanced at him uncertainly. Wade, in this mood, made her uneasy, but as he was still in his shirt and pants and she in her dress, there could be nothing to be really afraid of. She ignored his jibe. 'I want to talk to you about Miss Webb.'

'Not again!' With a low groan, he considered the glass he was holding before throwing down the contents in one go. 'See how you're driving me to drink?' he said grimly.

'No ...' she stuttered nervously, knowing he hadn't really asked a question but answering all the same. She watched the strong line of his throat as the last of his whisky disappeared, then her glance wandered to his jutting chin above which his mouth curved ruthlessly. She found herself suddenly unable to look away.

She heard him saying mockingly, 'I thought perhaps you'd come to continue what you started this afternoon?'

Vicki gasped, 'I started nothing!'

'No?' He was so frankly disbelieving she shivered, 'You held on so tight you might have put a limpet to shame.'

'You know that's not true!' She swallowed convulsively, wondering if it was. 'Anyway, that's not what I came to talk about.'

'I couldn't think of anything more entertaining,' he said softly, watching her closely. 'I've kissed quite a few women in my time—after all, it's quite an established custom—but I've never wanted to talk about it before. Curiously, I've a fancy to kiss you again, too.'

'Well, I haven't you,' Vicki muddled, trying, suddenly desperately, to hang on to the sensible sentences she had rehearsed in her room. 'I've never wanted to kiss you,' she added quickly.

'Liar!' His eyes hardened, but his voice was still soft.

'If you won't listen, I'd better go!' Her face colouring to a betraying pink, she turned, only to find herself caught by his hand.

'Oh, no you don't,' he said coolly. 'I've just mentioned that I've a fancy to kiss you. Liking needn't come into it.

And, as I don't believe you're averse to kissing me, I don't see why we shouldn't.'

'That's no reason!' she cried, her heart beginning to race in a way which frightened her. The blaze of hatred she had felt in him when he had first found her and brought her here had dulled to a less obvious glow, but was still there. He must have known how impossible it would be at Baccaroo to go on openly tearing each other apart, but she saw from the smouldering intensity of his eyes when he looked at her that his feelings for her hadn't changed. She was still the one who had thwarted his plans concerning his grandfather, the wife whose trickery had resulted in a son he didn't want. She must be made to pay, go on paying, if his austere expression was anything to judge by. His taunting of her like this was just another way of extracting revenge. She became conscious again of his rigorous regard, and faltered, 'You can't just go around kissing people as though it was a whim of the moment, to be satisfied as soon as it enters your head.'

As she turned, with every intention of leaving him, his arms were suddenly gripping her shoulders, forcing her around to face him. 'I can think of one reason at least. You're my wife, which surely gives me the right to do anything I like with you. Right now I could be interested in more than merely a few kisses.'

She stared up at him, unable to help herself, knowing he must see the pulse beating frantically in her throat. There were small flames in his eyes which flickered strangely as they rested on her. Apprehensively she shrank back, trying not to notice how her legs felt unaccountably weak. Somehow she must make him see sense.

'Please, Wade, let me go. I fully understand you never cared for me, not even when we were first married, but I can't believe you would ever act like a—an animal!'

'I'm simply a human one,' he said roughly. 'There's not much difference.'

'There has to be. You know there is!' But is there, a

small voice whispered darkly within her, when a man is
provoked too far? Surely, by coming fully dressed into
Wade's room, she hadn't done that? Yet the clamour in
her own body seemed to jeer, rather than reassure. 'Wade,'
she entreated, 'you married me for convenience. Why all
this, when you've always hated me?'

His laughter was harsh, his breath warm on her face.
'Maybe I still do, but not even you could deny a certain
magnetism between us. I've heard of it, but never believed
it existed. It happens only when I hold you, when I make
love to you, an incredible brilliancy of the senses. I realise
it doesn't happen with anyone else.'

'No, Wade, please!' That she felt terribly disturbed by
his mentioning this was obvious by her strangled cry of
protest, the dilated widening of her deep blue eyes. She
knew too well this instant response he talked of so frankly,
but it couldn't be anything to be taken seriously.

She drew an unsteady breath, holding herself perfectly
still, as if willing all feeling to leave her. 'You imagine
things,' she gulped. 'I never thought of you as being fanciful!'

Unfortunately this proved no discouragement. His eyes
taunted her, although he didn't again call her a liar. His
grip on her shoulders tightened, as he began, without words,
to punish her. A hand slid through her hair, pushing it
behind her ear, moving slowly over the fine skin of her
neck to her nape, his eyes examining each separate feature.
'You've changed. My God, how you've changed!' The
words seemed dragged out of him against his will. 'Your
hair—it's longer, beautiful. Your face isn't older, but it's
different. And your figure . . .'

'Wade!' Vicki stirred desperately, trying to inch away
from him, not knowing how much more of this she could
take. Not without betraying herself. Her eyes moved over
him compulsively. It was madness, she tried to convince
herself, to feel this way. There was a feeling going through
her that made her aware she hadn't told the truth when

she had hinted at hating him. Once before she had thought she had cared for him, but it had never been like this. Now she was conscious of a depth of love, a surge and sweep of wild desire, such as she had never before known. Nor did she know how to cope with it.

Her voice rose hysterically. 'Please, we have to talk about Miss Webb, Wade. Let me go!'

'To hell with Miss Webb!' he said, very clearly—and finally. His eyes stayed close. Under her hands, which pushed against him, Vicki could feel the hardness of his chest under his shirt. She also felt the heavy beat of his heart, and for one startled fascinated moment she went perfectly still.

That was a mistake; it gave him time to imagine she was waiting for something more. The anger of his last sentence was still in his face as he crushed her against him, as his mouth came cruelly against hers with a bruising intensity.

It was a kiss which, because of the hard passion behind it, had to end soon. Beneath the savage assault of Wade's mouth Vicki moaned, but when his head lifted it seemed there was worse to come. His hands began sliding her dress from her shoulders, dealing with zips and fasteners with decisive swiftness. When she fought him, he took no notice, simply imprisoned her hands and let his mouth wander over her bare fullness of her breasts. She could feel the feverish heat from his body, the helpless, answering warmth of her own, the wave of hot perspiration which dampened the skin his hands were exploring.

She felt his breath on her face, touching her closed eyes and burning cheeks, then he was kissing her again, lifting her, carrying her over the room. 'I want you in my bed,' he said thickly.

With a moan of protest she freed her mouth from his pitiless lips. 'Wade, this is madness!' she gasped.

He did not appear to have heard her. She found herself lowered on to the hard mattress, felt the pressure of him all over, but when she tried to tell herself this was all wrong, her hands touched his shoulders and clung.

Panting, she lay against him, the flame in his eyes burning her, urging her to complete submission, promising unspoken delight. Her heart accelerated madly and, of their own volition, her fingers sought the front of his shirt.

'Wait a minute.' His voice was a husky murmur, as he unbuttoned it himself, pulling it free of his belt. Next it was his belt which hit the floor. Then he was beside her again, and fire raced through her veins as his hungry mouth sought hers and his arms drew her ever closer.

Vicki knew she should try to avoid him somehow, that she should try to keep some common sense alive in her swimming head. Yet her resistance wavered under his primitive demands. Her strength weakened as his hands slid over her nakedness with rough, sensuous caresses that sent quivers right through her. His face blurred as she failed to keep it in focus. She thought she saw cruelty there, a desire to punish mixed with unleashed desire of another kind. No longer was there any gentleness in his hold and the beat of his heart was drumming fiercely into her own.

She closed her eyes as a sort of mindless bliss took over, as his mouth returned to crush her parted lips. His hands stroked her breasts, the soft seeking contours of her stomach and waist before lingering deliberately on her hips. The searing longing inside her for him to possess her, the awareness she had thought gone for ever, returned. The feverish response of her clinging arms and lips must have transmitted her intensely passionate need of him, for the intimate exploration of his hands deepened until she was lost in a world of sensual abandonment. Never could she remember that first time being as intense as this.

Vaguely she realised what she was inviting, but all sense of restraint seemed to leave her. Fear faded as her body moved, responding to his every touch. Her hands tangled in the dark hairs on his chest, slid over the muscles which rippled in his shoulders to lace tightly around his neck.

'You're beautiful,' he muttered hoarsely, his mouth plundering hers on a wave of hot desire. 'Vicki, do you want me as much as I think you do?'

'Yes,' she whispered, her agonised breath pleading, not trying to disguise her feelings any more. Her fear increased, but was not strong enough to fight such sensual excitement. 'Wade,' she murmured incoherently.

She heard him gasp, felt his whole body tense as he pulled her completely under him. There was pain, but her senses, clamouring for something they had searched for for so long, denied it. Then reality faded and everything was lost in a wild storm of sensual oblivion.

Later, when he whispered against her trembling mouth, 'This time I don't think you were disappointed?' she shook her dazed head, still floating in clouds. And when he drew her closer again, the hunger in their bodies not completely assuaged, she surrendered unashamedly.


When she woke the sun was streaming high in the sky and she was alone. As she became slowly aware of this she lay partly stunned. She was in Wade's bed, covered by a single crumpled sheet—a sheet which he had obviously thrown hurriedly over her. The rest of the bedclothes lay in a tumbled heap on the floor, silent proof that the night which had passed was not merely something dreamt up by a too vivid imagination.

Blindly Vicki stared about her as full realisation proceeded to hit her. The evidence of her own wanton behaviour was hard to accept. Bewildering pictures flashed through her mind, receiving humiliating attention. How could any of it have happened? She must have taken leave of her senses! Tearfully she tried to concentrate. She had come in here to discuss with Wade a few urgent matters which she had considered too imperative to wait. Things which could only be sorted out between the two of them and which should not have taken more than five minutes.

Yet somewhere, somehow, the conversation must have got out of hand.

Had it been her fault? Heat flowed through her as she suspected it might have been, simply by coming in here. What a fool she had been, playing right into Wade's hands. Now he would have every reason to despise her, to condemn her again as a tramp, and she couldn't altogether blame him. Hadn't he warned her, time and time again, to keep out of his way?

Feeling mortally humiliated by her own folly, Vicki crept out of bed. She was further shocked to find it was only an hour until lunch. What would everyone think? She would have to pretend she had felt ill. A cup of cold tea by the bedside made her blink. Wade must have brought it up before he went out. What, she wondered unhappily, was she supposed to conclude from that?

Her dress, lying on the floor under his shirt and trousers, made her blush. For once she was thankful Miss Webb's rigid morning routine didn't allow for Graham coming to seek his mother out. Perhaps, Vicki conceded doubtfully, there was something to be said for Miss Webb, after all.

Vicki had never thought her own room would prove a sanctuary, but this morning it did. Closing the door tightly behind her, she leant against it in a sudden trembling relief. She still found it difficult to believe those treacherous hours through the night had ever happened and could find little joy in recalling them. As for the love she had rediscovered, she found herself unable to face it. Already, only hours after the realisation of it, she was finding it made her heart ache almost unbearably. Wade might have shown her the ultimate joy of belonging to him. He was capable, she had discovered, of teaching her many things she had never known before, and had taken pleasure in arousing her. Why then, this morning, did she feel only bitterness?

As she showered she tried not to notice the red marks on her arms and limbs, the tears which streamed down with the water. Maybe she was getting too worked up.

Everything grew easier with time, even heartache. Wade, now he had taken his revenge, might leave her alone. That in itself, though she tried not to think of it, he might regard as further punishment, especially if he remembered her response to his lovemaking. To keep her at a distance would undoubtedly give him more satisfaction than having her in his bed again.

Putting on a thin cotton top and skirt, she brushed her hair quickly, plaiting it in a thick ponytail which hung half way down her slender back, making her look about fifteen. It was cooler this way. Then as the clock struck the half hour she ran downstairs. Her heart was still sore, but she was comforted that such a condition could be obvious to no one but herself.

Misilgoe was alone in the kitchen. Vicki threw her an apologetic smile as she placed the cup she had carried from the bedroom in the sink. 'I'm sorry I'm late,' she decided not to make a thing of it, 'I'm afraid I overslept.'

Misilgoe beamed happily. 'Missus must not worry. Miss Nurse been helping.'

'Miss Webb?' It wasn't impossible, but Vicki found it hard to believe.

'Yes, Mum,' Misilgoe's smile broadened. 'First thing Mr Wade sends her up with you'm cup of tea. "Take this up for my wife, Miss Webb", he says. Then, when she comes down, telling us you are still asleep, he orders her to help with lunch.'

Startled, Vicki stared at the girl, feeling her cheeks grow hot. 'Are you sure?' she stammered.

'Of course Misilgoe sure!' the girl nodded her dark curly head insistently. 'I was here, wasn't I?'

# CHAPTER EIGHT

'YES. Yes, of course.' Nodding her head without realising she was doing it, Vicki turned away before Misilgoe could see her flush with mortification. She was also trying to keep back a threatening wave of anger. Humiliation won, and she wished feverishly she could be like an ostrich and hide her head in the sand—well, at least hide her head, so she wouldn't have to encounter the calculating eyes of Miss Webb. What there would be in them Vicki wasn't sure, but Miss Webb would have had to be very blind indeed not to have come to certain conclusions when she had brought up that tea!

There wasn't even comfort to be gained from the knowledge that Miss Webb was technically staff, not paid to jump to conclusions. Miss Webb very rarely seemed to remember that, and her eyes, if expressionless, often hid curiosity if nothing else. How could Vicki tell her last night had been a mistake, one which wouldn't happen again?

Feeling herself going hot and cold in turn, Vicki went to the sink. Turning on the tap, she ran herself a glass of water, and gulped it down. It did little to sort out the mass of muddled thoughts which pursued her. Yet why get in such a state? Wasn't she legally Wade McLeod's wife—and generally husbands and wives did sleep together. She must allow that it was perhaps her own view of her marriage, more than anyone else's, that was at the root of her agitation. This, more than anything Miss Webb might have seen.

Plausible as this seemed, humiliation was still uppermost, and she wondered if Wade had set out deliberately to embarrass her. Otherwise why should he have sent Miss

Webb up with her tea, knowing of their clothing scattered over the floor, the tumbled state of the bed?

How could Vicki explain to Miss Webb that last night had been the accidental culmination of events which had somehow got beyond control? No—Vicki frowned, biting her lip. It wasn't something she could speak of to anyone, least of all Miss Webb. Even to think of doing so was ridiculous! She must just make sure she never went near Wade's room again. Last night she hadn't stopped to consider. If she had she wouldn't have believed Wade would have taken such a risk, not after what had happened last time. Perhaps, like her, he hadn't stopped to think.

Miss Webb was late in coming to lunch. She said it was because of having to help in the house that morning, thus getting behind with Graham's curriculum. She glanced at Vicki coldly, almost accusingly, and Vicki was annoyed to find herself looking away in confusion.

To make everything worse Wade walked in. He was so rarely in for a meal in the middle of the day that though there was plenty of food, she was not prepared for him and almost burst into hysterical tears. This she managed not to do, but the shock of having him sit down opposite, looking as coolly cynical as ever, was nearly too much. Her face went white and what little appetite she had appeared to vanish. It seemed she had been prepared for nothing this morning, at least nothing like this.

No one spoke immediately apart from Graham who, unless someone checked him, kept up an endless monologue of childish chatter. Apparently not curious as to why both his nurse and his mother had fallen so silent, he turned all his attention on his father.

Shooting a swift glance at Miss Webb, whose averted face betrayed clearly that some secret aspirations had been shattered, Vicki turned accusing eyes towards Wade. As their eyes met the quiet watchfulness in his changed derisively as he noted her expression.

'I trust you're feeling better this morning, Vicki?'

The sardonic inflection in his voice angered her again. How could he sit there enjoying his meal as if nothing had happened between them! He looked well. A lot of small lines seemed to have gone from his face and he looked somehow happier. Or was it just that he considered this whole affair a bit of a joke and was naturally amused by it? 'I feel much the same as usual,' she answered coldly.

Old Mr McLeod stirred himself. 'Got everything arranged for tomorrow, Wade?' he asked gruffly.

'All that's necessary,' Wade didn't look at his grandfather as he spoke but at Vicki, as if he knew quite well what was bothering her. 'It's been a bit of a rush. Jeff had some trouble with a bunch of cattle up in the wild country. I went and flushed them out with the chopper, but it still took time. I'd hoped to be back sooner.'

Vicki thought the Old Man must have been referring to something which concerned the station—Wade too. She was not prepared for the consternation inside her when the Old Man laughed.

'Don't have too many late nights while you're in Sydney, Wade.'

'Sydney?' Vicki's anger rose, then suddenly dissolved into something she couldn't name, unless it was fear. Her voice came quite shrill as compusively she stared at Wade. 'You were there only a few weeks ago.'

He replied curtly, glancing quickly at the others, as if impatient of their presence, 'You know, Vicki, I have to go there often—on business.'

'Yes.' Trying desperately to control herself, she subsided. Catching Miss Webb's faintly malicious smile, she realised she must have betrayed herself, yet the fact that Wade's wife was obviously among the last to learn of his departure didn't seem important any more. She felt deserted, that she was to be left on her own again. She even felt frightened—frightened and strangely heartbroken. 'How long will you be gone?' she gulped.

'Business shouldn't keep me longer than two or three days.' He stared at her narrowly.

'I'll wager you have other interests that will,' the Old Man broke in with a mischievous glance in Vicki's direction.

Other interests? Vicki felt a horrible coldness gripping her by the throat and felt suddenly ill again. The Old Man needn't spell it out, she had no need to ask! What a fool she had been to let herself hope, and this, she realised, was what she had been doing all along. She wasn't sure what exactly she had hoped for, but whatever it was it had suffered a crushing blow. Love and resentment warred within her, the latter winning, so that when she felt Wade's eyes on her she refused to look up.

Wade neither confirmed or denied his grandfather's sly digs regarding his stay in Sydney. Instead he said firmly, 'I'm taking you and Graham out after lunch, Vicki. I want to assure myself you haven't forgotten how to ride. You were good but inclined to be reckless, and in some ways I don't feel you've changed much.'

Why did she feel it wasn't just her riding he referred to? It must be a sign of something that he was prepared to spare her an hour of his valuable time. Most probably he merely wanted to be satisfied she was capable of being left in charge of Graham.

Before she could speak Miss Webb intervened. It was the first time she had opened her mouth to say anything during the meal, and then it was coolly. 'Graham usually has a little rest after lunch. I'm not sure we can manage.'

Wade smiled at her, quite indifferently. 'I'm going to give you the afternoon off, Miss Webb. I think you deserve it, and I'm sure Graham will suffer no harm if he misses his rest now and again. I'm sure you'll find something to fill in your time until we come back.'

It was astonishing that Miss Webb made no further demur. Vicki stared at her, as if willing her to find other objections, but all the nurse said was that she would get Graham ready.

Vicki wanted to refuse Wade's offer urgently, to remind him how, when he had literally dragged her from Melbourne, her entertainment had never been on the schedule he had planned for her. Of course he hadn't said it was for this reason he had arranged the afternoon. Very probably she would find it far from entertaining.

When he asked curtly if she had done any riding since she had left she could have wept that he made no attempt, in front of Miss Webb, to hide that they had been apart. For all she lost patience with herself for caring she answered sharply, 'Don't worry, I shan't make a nuisance of myself by being thrown.' She almost added—which will eliminate any possibility of having to keep me here longer than necessary, with broken bones! There was something about the set of his mouth, however, that warned her that such observations might be better kept to herself. A faint hope of a last-minute reprieve came to her. 'What about your grandfather?' she tried to be tactful. 'He might want me here.'

'I can manage,' the Old Man grunted, not for a moment deceived. 'If I die while you're gone I'm not going to take any harm until you get back.'

Wade snapped harshly, as if this was the last thing he cared about, 'Jeff's here, and Miss Webb.'

Vicki forbore to point out that he had given Miss Webb the afternoon off. She had long since realised the futility of arguing with him, so just confined herself to staring at him resentfully.

He rose to his feet. 'I've just one or two things left to see to. You'd better get one of the girls to put up a cool drink for Graham and something to eat. We might be gone some time.'

For all he said this, Vicki had not expected they would be going any great distance because of Graham's age. She was startled, therefore, to find they were taking the helicopter and there was no sign of any horses.

'You said riding!' she exclaimed, frowning at him over Graham's small, wriggling body.

'So I did,' he replied shortly, 'and so we are. Maybe you didn't hear me mention that the boys are busy combing out the wild country for strays. Well, that's where we're going. We can pick up three horses there.'

'I don't know why you're doing this,' she attacked him tautly. 'I wouldn't have come, but——' she couldn't go on until she'd taken a very deep breath, 'there's something I want to speak to you about and there might not be another chance, as you're going away.'

'Really?' His voice was taunting, the expression in his eyes savagely mocking as they went slowly, assessingly over her. They seemed to strip her coldly and, by direct contrast, her whole body went hot. 'When I suggested this trip it was for Graham's amusement. I'm taking the chopper because of his age. Wherever we go we can't be away long, but I think he's already explored many of the creeks around the homestead.'

'Yes, but——'

He cut in ruthlessly, 'Whatever you have to say to me will have to wait until we're alone or he's at a safe distance.'

Already Graham was looking from one to the other, a little of his excitement giving way to bewilderment as he sensed, without understanding, that his parents were quarrelling. It was a perception which must be born in children as he had never known two parents until recently. In spite of her love for him, Vicki found herself regarding him with an impatience she had to stifle. Glancing at Wade again, she agreed sullenly. 'Oh, all right. Perhaps it's just as well we'll soon be back. I realise you must be busy, what with having to arrange your trip tomorow, as well as everything else.'

'I didn't arrange anything,' he replied cryptically.

She looked down at her tightly clasped fingers, none the wiser, finding it impossible to look for clues in the dark

hardness of his face. Suddenly she dared not look at him.
Her memories of last night, while wrapped in a hazy veil
of sensuous sensation, were too recent. Something in her
face, she feared, would betray her, if she were to meet his
devious glance too often. It was strange, she thought, how
for over four years memories seemed all she had had to
cling to. For her there had never been the rosy hopes for
the future on which most people based their most constant
reflections. With a painful sigh she turned to her small son,
putting her arm protectively around him as the helicopter
veered.

That Graham was obviously not scared at all and was
thrilled to the tips of his small boots seemed just something
else to hold against Wade. Vicki's distraught face closed
up as she glanced down at his dancing excitement.

'Was this really necessary?' she asked quickly, as Wade
bent enquiringly towards her. 'It's only going to make
everything more difficult for him, one day soon.'

Wade didn't pretend not to understand what she meant,
and his eyes narrowed slightly. 'I didn't say anything about
his leaving.'

As he placed a heavy emphasis on his second last word,
Vicki felt herself shake. So her suspicions could be right?
Wide with an unspoken accusation, her eyes flew to his
and she saw in them all the old cruelty.

Becoming aware of Graham's sulky face gazing at her,
she was ready to decide tearfully that he was beginning to
dislike her as much as Wade obviously did. Realising this,
she was quite prepared to hear him say crossly, 'Graham's
staying at Baccaroo, Mummy.'

'I'm staying——' she automatically corrected him, and
was startled when Wade apparently busy with the controls,
retorted tersely,

'You'd better wait until you're asked.'

They reached the camp by mid-afternoon and the horses
were already waiting.

There was a small pony for Graham. 'I had it brought

up with the stock horses,' Wade told Vicki briefly, his face still hard, as though the harshness of his last remark still lingered between them.

There was not a great deal to be seen at the stock camp and she was relieved when they mounted and left, glad to escape from the constant admiration in the cook's eyes as they rested on her while he ostensibly helped the boss. Wade had told them on their way here that his grandfather had always been very insistent about hunting out cattle that wandered away from the main herds and took to living wild. It had certainly been almost an essential way of supplementing income in the harder times the McLeod family had known. The Old Man was still keen, so was Jeff Curry. Wade confessed to occasionally enjoying a few days spent this way himself, but Vicki doubted if it was to indulge his grandfather.

As they rode off she heard Wade explaining to Graham, who seemed to understand such things, that they brought on such expeditions plenty of stock horses and a small mob of quieter cattle. Then the men would ride into the thick bush-covered gullies and creeks to find the wild ones. Sometimes they might be forced to chase some of these animals for miles, until the beast eventually turned on them. Then the rider had to fling himself off his horse and pull it down, then tie the cow or bull's legs together. After this the man would return to base camp and bring back a few of the tamer cattle. Usually the captured animal, once its leg ties were removed, would allow itself to be driven with the others back to camp.

Vicki wondered, listening to Graham's many questions, why Wade didn't mention the danger. Unhappily she was aware, as she had been once before, that she could be jealous. She noticed how Graham's interest was wholly caught by what his father was telling him, that his reactions were entirely different from the childish if innocent boredom he had usually displayed when she had talked to him of her days at the shop.

'Don't you think you should point out how dangerous it is?' she said stiffly. 'Flinging yourself off a horse to grab a wild bull by its tail?'

'They aren't always bulls, or terribly wild.' Wade shot her a comprehending glance, glinting with ironic amusement 'Perhaps he's been shielded a bit too much. You can't recognise danger if you don't know it exists. But it will be years yet before he can go chasing after anything on his own.'

As if to demonstrate that he wasn't as irresponsible as she made out he kept Graham on a leading rein, refusing to let him off even when the boy objected. 'You're on a strange pony,' he said. 'He's not what you've been used to.'

Vicki, her eyes going from the man, so tall in the saddle, to the young child by his side, wasn't sure she was pleased at the way Graham rode. For a four-year-old he was quite remarkable and she supposed such an aptitude must be in his blood. Despairingly she reflected that while the way Graham was shaping constantly delighted old Mr McLeod and earned his father's approval, it failed to bring her the same satisfaction. More and more his father and great-grandfather would be determined he should never leave Baccaroo. She was not so certain of Wade, but there seemed to have been a different light in his eyes when he had looked at Graham lately. Desperately Vicki hoped she was mistaken.

There could be no disputing that the country here was wild. There was something about it which thrilled Vicki yet made her shiver. Maybe because it was so hard and ruthless it bred men, who of necessity were made the same way— otherwise they might never survive. She had, for all its harshness, come to love it, but some parts, she thought wryly, were worse than others. At the homestead this was always referred to as the wild country. It was here that cattle often strayed. They could be lost for months, sometimes years, until there was a need or inclination to hunt them out. Occasionally small planes were used for this purpose nowadays, but horses were often the only satis-factory way of completing the job.

Once Wade had brought her out here for a couple of days. She had enjoyed every minute of it. He didn't ask if she remembered, so she didn't mention it. One part of that short expedition was better forgotten, anyway.

She recalled that it had been very hot and they had found a half wild steer and chased it through the bush. She had lost her hat and had stopped. Wade had noticed im-mediately and left Jeff to get on with the chasing while he had turned back to help her retrieve it.

There had been a trickle of water in a dried-up creek bed, only a trickle, but she had begged to be allowed to rinse her hot face in it, after they had found her hat.

As he had nodded she had dismounted and Wade had slid from his own horse to watch her. He had walked over to her, glancing at her closely, with an intentness she had found disconcerting. Then, to her astonishment, as she got to her feet again, he had reached for her, and drawn her into his arms.

It had been a terrible shock to her over-excited heart as he had pulled her close and buried his face against her warm young neck. She had only to close her eyes to feel still the heat from his body, the overwhelmingly sensuous feeling which had shot through her as he had crushed her to his sweat-soaked chest. She had found herself clinging to him as his arms had suddenly tightened. He had picked her up, with a thicky muttered exclamation, and began carrying her deeper among the trees. Her clinging hands had wrapped themselves around his neck and she had turned up her mouth, searching blindly but instinctively for his. Then the enraged steer had broken through on them.

Even now, although trying to convince herself it didn't matter, she found herself wondering what would have hap-pened if the beast hadn't doubled back. She recalled how, as if suddenly coming to his senses, Wade had almost thrust

her away from him. It had been a long time before he had
touched her again. That had been early in their marriage.

Jerking back to the present, she heard Graham crying
that the boulders they were passing were on fire. She
smiled. This was exactly what she had thought herself when
she had first come out here. Both the sandy scrub and
mountains of Central Australia were the colour of terra-
cotta. This was the red centre, the hundreds of miles of
desert and semi-arid plains which made up a lot of the
great Outback, the land of the never-never! This was a
part of the huge continent where a torrential rain of
twelve inches or more could be followed by three years of
drought. And, with no rain at all, cattle could begin dying
in their hundreds.

Today, with the heat rebounding off the dried-up earth
and rocks, she wondered how Graham stood it after the
almost English climate of Melbourne. 'Are you all right?'
she asked anxiously, but he never so much as blinked a
sandy eyelash, as he nodded his head.

Funny, she reflected, those thick, camelhair lashes were
all Graham appeared to have inherited from her. In everything else he was Wade. A deep depression smote her. This
wasn't something she hadn't known, but coming here had
made it infinitely worse. When eventually she managed to
escape with him, every time she looked at him she would
see Wade, the husband who didn't want her. How, she
asked herself desperately, would she ever learn to live with
it? Before it hadn't seemed to matter so much, but it was
different now.

The creek Wade took them to was the same one she had
just recalled, but she couldn't believe he had brought her
here deliberately. Today there was a little more water in
it, but it was still no more than a few feet across. Graham
protested he would rather try to catch a wild cow, but his
father said he must content himself by the pool, that there
would be no wild 'cows' for him until he was much older.

Wade chose a spot where there was shade from trees. It

was sparse, but it was shade and a welcome relief. With a relieved sigh Vicki sank down under one of the overhanging branches, the tiredness which had pursued her since she had got up coming over her again. She didn't realise how very young she looked in her brief shirt and tight pants, her hair falling heavy and silken on either side of her clear-cut, unblemished face.

Graham, resigning himself to the water, splashed happily. After seeing to the horses, Wade had a word with him before coming over to stare down at Vicki.

'Tired?'

Something in his eyes caused her to flush warmly. 'I don't know why you ask,' she retorted mutinously. 'You know I'm never tired.'

'I don't know anything of the sort,' he rejoined coolly. 'I seem to remember when you and Graham first arrived you were very tired indeed. If I hadn't insisted you have plenty of rest you wouldn't have made such a good recovery. As it is, I still see you occasionally looking too pale.'

She doubted if he ever really noticed, although she did admit how, after finding her on the point of collapse on the day she had been cleaning her bedroom, he had looked after her, even if his usual harsh manner hadn't changed. For a while, until she had grown stronger, he had often been around. Now, as he settled his long length beside her, she wished he would take himself away. She had no desire to have an unrestricted view of his broad chest, as he unbuttoned his shirt against the heat and lay back with his arms negligently behind his head.

'I'm going to ask you something else,' he resumed dryly, when she didn't speak. 'I'd like to know what's eating you this afternoon. Apart from a smouldering sense of injustice, which is obvious a mile off, I'm convinced there's something else. Correct me if I'm wrong, madam, but I don't think so.'

Staring away from him, she found herself unable to deny it. 'No—you're right, but I don't know why I should have to put it into words.' She kept her voice down so Graham wouldn't hear. He was young enough to be fond of repeating things and she didn't want him filling Miss Webb's ears.

'Put what into words?' Wade's voice was low, too, but infinitely savage.

Beneath his hard eyes she almost hadn't the nerve to go on. She nearly didn't, but it was bursting to be out, she couldn't seem to do anything to stop it. Her cheeks were scarlet as she opened dry lips. 'Why did you send Miss Webb with my tea this morning? It's not something you usually concern yourself with. I don't think I shall ever be able to look her in the face again!'

'It was what you wanted, wasn't it?'

'What I wanted?' Vicki's eyes widened with indignation. 'What on earth do you mean?'

'I'm talking about what she obviously saw,' Wade retorted with harsh impatience. 'Now she'll stop wondering about our marriage, stop seeing herself as the second Mrs McLeod and be able to concentrate on her job.'

Trembling, Vicki stared at him, her hot cheeks growing rapidly colder. The second Mrs McLeod! So already he was letting her know indirectly that there was to be one!

'That's what you were in such a hurry to see me about last night, wasn't it?' he insisted dryly. 'You can't make me believe it wasn't important, not when it forced you to come into my bedroom.'

'Yes.' There seemed no point in denying it further. Only now it seemed possible she had been stupid to imagine a talk with him would have solved anything. She had been silly to allow Miss Webb to put her in such a wild panic. 'I did want to speak to you about Miss Webb, but it wasn't anything you could have known about.'

'No?' He didn't spare her. 'Don't you think I've seen the speculation in her eyes, the uncertainty in yours, every time she looks from me to you? I doubt it you'll ever be a match for the Miss Webbs of this world, but this wasn't your major problem, was it? Most of all you were scared that I was attracted to her, weren't you, and determined to confront me with the despicableness of my regrettable behaviour?'

'If I was,' Vicki cried, her face burning with confusion, 'it was merely because I don't want any scandal, for Graham's sake.'

'For Graham's sake! Don't you think it's about time you faced a few facts, my dear? You soon forgot about your son last night, in my arms.'

'You're a fiend!' she choked, clenching her hands tight, pressing one unconsciously over her shaking lips.

'That—and perhaps other things you're not honest enough to admit,' he returned grimly. 'I didn't anticipate your nocturnal visit, so you can't blame me entirely for what happened. When a man has someone like you in his bedroom it's maybe understandable that he should lose his head. Especially if the lady is willing!'

Vicki tried to ignore his hard sarcasm, tried also to ignore that he might be speaking the truth. Her only remaining comfort was that she surely couldn't have acted as shamelessly as he implied. 'What you did was bad enough,' she muttered bitterly, 'without taking it any further.'

'So!' His hands left the back of his head to shoot out and grip her averted shoulders. 'What if I did? The way your mind works, madam, is sometimes beyond my comprehension. It certainly seemed to do the trick, sending Miss Webb up with your tea. You could thank me for thinking of it. It did away with the need for any embarrassing confrontation, if that was what you were after. Embarrassing for you and Miss Webb, mind you, not me. Women like Miss Webb never worry me, not one bit.'

'No,' Vicki swallowed, wriggling from his hold, 'I'm sure they don't!'

'Just what exactly do you mean by that?' His voice jarred in her ear, low and threatening with anger. 'I've taken about all I'm going to take from you. You mustn't realise whom you're getting at!'

'The great Wade McLeod! Oh ...' Her small, startled exclamation was rudely cut off as he pulled her backwards into his arms and his mouth came down swiftly to crush hers. She felt his hand sliding over her, reminding her sharply of the first time they had come here, but now his touch was different. It was full of a far more intimate knowledge of her than it had ever held then.

Mercifully, she felt, Graham's cry from the creek interrupted the deepening pressure of his lips. The glint in Wade's eyes, however, when he released her, spoke of ironic amusement at her obvious agitation—not of remorse. Graham wanted to catch a fish but couldn't find one. He wanted to take off his clothes and swim. Then he decided he was hungry.

Realising he was probably too tired for any of these things, Vicki went and put a loving arm around him while Wade poured him a cool drink. She felt strange.

As he went for their horses Wade said evenly, 'It won't have done him any harm if he did see me kissing you. I didn't plan it deliberately and I'm sorry it happened, but I hadn't forgotten he was there.'

'It doesn't matter,' she whispered, scarcely knowing what she was saying. 'I don't really care.'

'That I bloody well realise!' he exclaimed, with a low violence which almost frightened her.

All the way back to the base camp Vicki felt numb. Wade took Graham up in front of him for the return journey. Having to follow the two figures who meant more to her than anyone else didn't help Vicki feel any better. She even found it difficult to share in the men's amusement when, on being lowered from his father's horse, Graham muttered, 'Strewth!' in true Australian fashion. And when they asked what sort of time he'd had, he replied solemnly, 'Fair dinkum, thank you.' How she wished Wade's glance of amused tolerance had been directed at her!

In spite of his attempts at adult nonchalance, Graham

slept in her arms as they returned to the homestead, his rumpled dark brown head cuddled against her shoulder.

Wade said very little, but as he brought the helicopter gently to rest he turned to glance at them grimly. 'You both look about the same age. Sometimes I find it hard to tell the difference.'

The night wind was bringing a small measure of welcome coolness as they reached the house. They had been gone longer than Vicki had expected and Miss Webb gazed at her reproachfully as she saw Graham's tired face. Vicki, remembering in time Wade's sarcastic remarks about her being too meek to make a good mistress, felt guilty but didn't apologise. For such endeavour she thought she caught a glimpse of approval in his eyes, the eyes which only a few minutes ago she had been unable to read.

It didn't seem to make sense that she hadn't found an opportunity to speak to him about Sydney while they had been out. Or was it that the chance had been there, but she'd been too nervous to take it? Even now Vicki wasn't quite sure what she wanted to say, but for some reason she couldn't quite fathom, it seemed imperative she mention it. When Wade disappeared immediately after dinner she thought she would find him in the office.

After helping Misilgoe with the dishes and checking that everything was finished for the night she knocked on the office door. To her disappointment Jeff Curry was there alone and, after chatting for a short time, she returned to the house. Jeff was nice but, like Miss Webb, was obviously curious about Vicki and Wade, and this made Vicki uneasy. Especially when, in the past, Jeff had proved a true friend. Meeting his frankly anxious gaze as she left him, she felt positively mean.

As Wade didn't seem to be anywhere she decided to forget about Sydney. She still didn't know what she wanted to say about his trip anyway.

Old Mr McLeod, she found, had retired to bed. Miss Webb, she already knew, having struck up a friendship

with one of the stockmen's wives, had popped out to see
her. As she had promised, Vicki looked in on Graham and
found, as she expected, that he was fast asleep, tired out
by the exertions and excitement of his day. Bending down,
she kissed his flushed cheek, feeling the warmth of her love
for him spilling over.

Then Miss Webb was there, but instead of going immediately to her own room, Vicki went along to Mr Mc-
Leod's. He seemed so alone these days. Vicki hadn't been
back long before she had realised he was really just a
pathetic old man and, for all his grunts and snarls, was
more in need of love and pity than anything else. For her
the past had not the same reality it still apparently held for
Wade, but she could see no sense in keeping old bitterness
alive, to the extent that it poisoned all their lives. In this,
she realised, the Old Man himself was far from guiltless,
but she found she could forgive him. Each night, now, she
went to his room to see if there was anything she could do
for him.

To her surprise, because he usually waved her away, he
asked if she would get him a drink. Knowing exactly what
he meant, but disapproving, she brought hot milk. For a
moment she thought he was going to explode, then he
astonished her by drinking it, almost meekly. After this
he wanted his pillows straightened and his light put off. It
was nearly half an hour later before Vicki reached her own
bedroom.

Wade was not yet in his, or if he was he must have gone
straight to bed, as there was complete silence. Vicki was
tired to the point of weariness. It was only her body that
felt curiously alive and restless. Knowing she might not
sleep if she couldn't rid herself of the feeling of being
deserted, she removed her long dress and took a shower.
Afterwards she slipped into her silky pyjamas and got into
bed. There was a tightness of tears in her throat, even
though she knew she would be wiser to forget about the
previous night. Wade, she was convinced, would never

bother her again. Wasn't his hurried flight to Sydney a silent but very emphatic declaration of this?

The next minutes passed slowly. She tried to sleep, but found it impossible as she was so tense. Why she should be feeling so tense—and deserted—she couldn't think. It made no sense at all, considering everything. When the door of her room opened and Wade walked through, as if he had every right to be there, everything inside her seemed to dissolve in a terrible turmoil. She wasn't surprised at it, but she found it almost impossible to bear the coldness in his eyes as he stood looking down at her.

For a long moment he studied her stricken confusion, meeting the wide bewilderment in her eyes with harsh mockery. 'I thought to find you in my bed, not here,' he sneered.

'Why should I?' she gasped, his hardness acting as a brake to an impulsive inclination to throw herself into his arms. As always she longed for his tenderness. Since she had realised the depth of her love for him, the hurt of his imperviousness was almost more than she could take.

'I wouldn't have thought you need ask that, not after last night,' he said frostily. 'You met me more than half-way, but I see you still want to believe it was all my doing.'

Dropping on to the edge of the bed, he grasped her wrist. He wore only a light robe over pyjama trousers and as his hand gripped her every nerve in her body cried out in panic and she tried to avert her eyes. 'I don't have to answer that!'

As if he was seeking to control himself, his gaze flickered narrowly, then left her to stare darkly around the room. The lines around his mouth etched deeply and his hard jaw set, as if he found nothing in the bare precincts of it to please him. 'I suppose,' he shrugged, 'I've lain here long nights, knowing you were next door. It takes a bit of under-standing.'

Vicki turned sharply back to him, unsure of his meaning yet feeling it should tell her something. But what he said next confused and bewildered her even more.

'Vicki,' he said dryly, his attention riveted on her again, taking in all her fair young beauty, 'I didn't come here to quarrel with you, or to insist, if you weren't willing, on my marital rights. I came to ask if you would like to go to Sydney with me tomorrow.'

# CHAPTER NINE

'Go to Sydney with you?' Vicki repeated, feeling stunned. He couldn't really mean it, or could he? Her startled eyes, searching his compulsively, met the usual coldness. which brought sudden enlightenment. 'I suppose you want me to come for fear I try to run off with Graham while you're gone? Now I know why you tried to be pleasant earlier this afternoon! You're frightened to leave me in case something like this happens and the shock proves too much for your grandfather!'

'Vicki!'

His leashed exclamation didn't warn her. It might have done, but her fevered brain wasn't listening. It was too busy jumping to more damning conclusions, rushing on ... 'Or did you plan to leave me in Sydney? Dump me, with no money to find my way back? I always knew you were no good, Wade McLeod, but I never thought you would stoop to such great depths!'

'Are you quite finished?' he asked frigidly, his eyes black.

She was, but only because she had no breath left to continue. It was as if every flicker of it had been drawn from her trembling body to leave her gasping.

Quite deliberately he lifted his hand to slap her across the face, but she raised her own arm in time to stop him. They glared angrily at each other for one long moment. The expression in his eyes was terrifying.

'Oh!' Wildly she flinched away from him, a cry of fright escaping her as he roughly took hold of her.

'I've never tried to slap a woman before, Vicki. 'But you seem to bring out my basest instincts.' God help me, but you almost drive me to murder! If you despise me as much as you obviously do, you could be wiser to keep your thoughts to yourself. I have to go to Sydney on business, you little fool.'

'What about what your grandfather said?' she cut in
sharply, anger now mingling with apprehension causing
a fine recklessness. 'He didn't give the impression that you
were going for any other reason than to enjoy yourself.'

Wade's smile was cruel, his eyes without mercy on the
hectic colour in her cheeks. 'That I'm certainly going to do
now. And as you don't want any more of my company,
don't be surprised if I bring someone back with me.' His
broad shoulders lifted as he pushed her away from him
and rose from the bed. 'As for escaping with your son,
madam, I shouldn't advise you to waste your time trying.
You wouldn't get very far.'

Next morning Vicki saw him leave, but he never spoke
or looked once in her direction. She didn't see the white
ring around his mouth as he glanced at her briefly while
she was speaking to Graham. Graham was tearful that his
father was going but excited by Wade's promise to bring
him something back. He had never been brought back a
present before, he said. Then his small face fell again as
Wade refused to promise when this would be.

Old Mr McLeod was restless all the time Wade was
away, and Vicki, intensely unhappy, found him difficult
to bear. He took to demanding that Graham should be with
him continually, but fearing this wouldn't be good for either
of them, Vicki put her foot down. She decreed that they
should go on as usual and, when the Old Man fretted, took
to spending quite a lot of time with him herself. This way
Miss Webb's careful curriculum wasn't too interrupted by
his constant demands.

Graham had been with him that afternoon and Vicki sent
him out to get some fresh air with Miss Webb. She would
have liked to go with them, but contented herself with
sitting with Mr McLeod on the verandah. Wade had been
gone for almost a week. Bleakly she wondered what he
was doing.

'He's probably gone to Nooanda.' The Old Man might have guessed her thoughts and she felt her face pale. Nooanda was another cattle station the McLeods owned. It lay on the Macdonnell Ranges, due west of Alice Springs. Vicki had never been there, but she knew it was a part of the country which the famed Namitjira had often painted.

As she stoically nodded her head, the Old Man went on, 'On the other hand, he knows a lot of people in Sydney.' Suddenly, to her surprise, his eyes were troubled, rather than malicious. 'Does it worry you, Victoria, that Wade might be chasing other women?'

It took Vicki a moment to steady herself sufficiently to speak. Both his question and his use of her full name un-nerved her. It was the first time she had heard him address her as anything and, while conscious it might not mean much, she felt strangely moved. His question, she sensed, held none of his usual spite. He seemed aware of the pain it caused and oddly sympathetic. It astonished her that he was prepared to unbend even this much. She was even more confused by her own willingness to forget how much he had wounded her in the past. For the first time she could remember she felt they were seeking to comfort each other because of Wade, yet she couldn't restrain a peculiar desire to defend him.

'I've been away for over four years, Mr McLeod. It seems logical to suppose he might have formed other attach-ments.'

'If you can't speak in plain language, Victoria, don't speak at all!' the Old Man muttered querulously. Then he looked at her, his old face sad with shame. 'I'm sorry, my dear,' he took a deep breath, making an almost visible effort to go on, 'I think I should maybe be sorry for a lot of things—concerning you, concerning Wade. Sometimes I feel I've detracted from the extra years that have been given to me.'

Vicki smiled at him gently but had more sense than

to comment on that. Something warned her to be cautious, not to take too much for granted straight away. He was a wily old fox at the best of times and, as with Wade, she must guard herself from further hurt,

'Maybe,' he shot an anxious glance at her under bushy white brows, 'maybe it was my fault you ran off as you did? Wade never said so—well, not exactly, but I've often wondered.'

'No, it wasn't. It had nothing to do with you.' At least this was the truth, she didn't have to prevaricate. 'You didn't make my life any easier, but I probably understood better than you think. But no, you didn't drive me away.'

'Perhaps,' he grunted, his crinkled old eyes keen for all his advanced years, 'I've a good idea what did, which makes it my fault, if only indirectly.'

Vicki bit her lip.

'I'd like you to know, my dear, just what it means to me that Wade has a son and how much I appreciate having him here.'

Again she could think of nothing to say.

He glanced at her, with a faint return of the craftiness she feared. 'I only wish Graham had a brother. Probably in time——?'

'I'm afraid——' Vicki began, then halted, flushing painfully. She had been about to tell him sharply that it wasn't possible. That he must know surely Wade meant to divorce her. Now she wondered why she couldn't go on. She did manage to say briefly, 'I shouldn't bank on it.'

'Never mind,' the Old Man's unsteady hand came out to pat hers almost kindly, 'I'm content, and I'm grateful to you, Victoria, that I'll be able to die that way.'

Partly because of this conversation with his grandfather, whenever Vicki thought of Wade in the days which followed a deep confusion beset her. She knew an unbelievably deep regret that she hadn't gone to Sydney with him. All that night, after he had asked her, she had lain awake wishing she had the courage to go to him and ask his forgiveness, tell him she had changed her mind. This she had found impossible, but she had resolved to beg him to take her with him in the morning. This, of course, proved equally impossible, after one glance at his implacable face.

Now, as she wondered if he would ever come back, she realised there was little joy in anything for her any more, when she was apart from him. Not even Graham's lively, lovable presence could make up for Wade's absence.

The doctor called one evening on his way back to Alice Springs. It was not Frank Evans; apparently he had moved on and, while she missed seeing him, she felt strangely relieved. He and Wade had been friendly and he had known so much about her. He wouldn't have asked questions, but she would have had to endure his curious glances, and she had had too many of those to put up with.

Before he went the new doctor contrived to speak to her discreetly. 'Mr McLeod's not too good,' he said frankly, as she walked to the door with him.

'I've felt that.' Vicki spoke anxiously, having noticed herself how easily tired he became, how, in spite of trying not to, he slept the greater part of each day. 'My husband is away, but I'm sure he would return if ...'

'No immediate need, Mrs McLeod,' the man looked at her kindly. 'I don't think there's anything you can do for him, more than you're already doing, and your husband has been keeping in touch. Mr McLeod's condition hasn't really changed. It's just that I can read other small signs.'

'How long would you give him?'

'Well,' he smiled faintly, 'there's very rarely a specific answer to that one. One can never tell, especially with a man like him. It could be days—or weeks.'

In spite of the doctor's reassurances, Vicki couldn't help being worried. She found it difficult to know if she was doing enough. The Old Man hated people fussing over him, but it seemed necessary to keep him under fairly constant surveillance. When she gave an evasive answer as to what the doctor had been saying to her, he merely laughed and replied that there was still a lot of life left in him yet!

Miss Webb was a great help and, as they grew friendly, Vicki came to like and appreciate her. The nurse, she discovered, had many good qualities. It was she who insisted that Vicki go out for an hour each afternoon. She said Vicki was too white and would not be much good to anyone if she did not have some relaxation.

So, while Miss Webb kept an eye on Mr McLeod, she and Graham went riding. Jeff Curry often came with them. Whether by accident or design he was usually around when they went to seek their horses and Vicki felt she couldn't very well object to his company. During the short time they were out they talked idly, always of things which didn't matter. Somehow she couldn't bear mentioning anything that did, even though she often longed to talk to somebody.

Then Wade was back. He was in touch, flying from Alice. When Jeff came up to the house to tell them Vicki felt a surge of joy mixed with relief. She felt tense with a wild elation and had to turn away as tears sprang to her starry eyes. Doing this she missed the expression of discomfort on Jeff's face.

Stiffly he told Mr McLeod, 'I'm taking the truck out to meet them—thought you'd like to know, sir.'

'Meet them?' Vicki swung around sharply, but didn't immediately suspect anything. 'He isn't alone, then?'

'No——' Jeff stared at her and suddenly she hated his air of embarrassment. 'He asked me to tell you Miss Morris is with him, and to have her room prepared.'

When he was gone Vicki didn't look at Mr McLeod. She turned and ran straight upstairs. In a peculiar, dazed fashion she stumbled blindly to the room Miss Morris usually occupied, stopping just outside the door. It was here that she had met Wade coming out of it on that night long ago. It had been here that he had kissed her for the first time. Half sobbing, she recalled it vividly. Not until then had she realised exactly what a kiss could do.

Drawing a deep breath in an effort to stop weeping, she rubbed a hand over her wet eyes. So he had carried out his threat. He was bringing a woman back with him, moreover, one he knew well. Was Miss Morris to be his next wife, Hadn't he warned her that as soon as his grandfather passed on they would be divorced, and hadn't she agreed? Agreed blindly, little realising just what it would do to her, but she certainly had never expected he would bring his next bride here until she had gone.

Seeking Misilgoe, she instructed her to air and dust the room. It was a beautifully appointed room, much nicer than the one Vicki occupied, but she felt too numb to be envious. She made up the bed herself with the best linen then carefully closed the door. Miss Morris should be quite comfortable!

She was downstairs, cold with a kind of artificial composure, to greet them when they arrived. Leoda Morris was blooming and looked no older than when Vicki had last seen her. Laughing, she hung on to Wade's arm as they came through the open verandah into the drawing room.

The Old Man was delighted to see their new guest and made no attempt to hide it. 'How are you, my dear?' he smiled at the radiant Leoda, who bent to offer him her cool hand. 'I'm delighted to see you. How is your dear mother?'

Vicki tried, but couldn't keep the bitterness from her eyes as Wade stooped down to speak to Graham, who had rushed in, aglow with excitement. No one apparently realised she existed.

With determination she stared away from him, finding it easier to concentrate on Miss Morris. At least Miss Morris didn't make her feel as if something was tearing the very heart from her body.

Wade didn't like being ignored. His hand shot out, before she had taken more than her first step. He caught her wrist and she was aware he could feel how her pulse was jerking and racing. As she silently hated him for being so devious he said, under cover of Graham's furious chatter, 'Hello, Vicki. How have you been?'

'Very well.' She still didn't look at him. Never, now, must he be allowed to see how much she cared.

'Missed me?' His voice was low but beat insistently on her sensitive ears. He had a nerve, sounding as if it really mattered that she had!

Quickly she shook her fair, glistening head. 'No!'

His eyes glinted, but he let it go. He even dropped her wrist, as if not interested any more. 'Grandfather hasn't been so good, I believe?'

'No.' She made an effort. 'He hasn't been confined to bed ...' Why were they talking like this, like two strangers? Desperately Vicki tried to stop her eyes from clinging to Wade's dark face, his tall, broad-shouldered figure. He wore a pair of light tan pants with a smart shirt and tie and she felt her breath catch somewhere in her lower regions. He had no right to look so devastatingly attractive!

Miss Morris came back to them, holding out an elegant hand. Her smile was cool, as wholly condescending as ever it had been, regarding Vicki. 'How are you, my dear child? You've come up in the world since I last saw you.'

'Or down.' For sheer effrontery, Miss Morris had always taken some beating,

'Oh, I wouldn't say that! I think you've done very well for yourself.'

Vicki swallowed hard. 'Depending on how one looks at it. I hope you're keeping well, Miss Morris?'

'Oh, call me Leoda,' Miss Morris smiled brilliantly, not at all put out, when Vicki's frankness matched her own. 'We must have some time together, you and I.'

'Are you planning to stay long?' Vicki forced an answering smile. She felt ashamed to be asking such a question yet couldn't keep it back. If it was impertinent she doubted Miss Morris would notice. This was, after all, a land where hospitality was almost taken for granted.

'I hadn't made any plans.' Miss Morris wrapped her arm around Wade's again, smiling up at him. 'It will depend on Wade, here, won't it, darling?'

Vicki felt sick and the contempt in her eyes showed as she looked at them. She hadn't really expected him to, but Wade had made no attempt to protect her from Leoda Morris's pointed remarks. He was glancing down at the woman now, with a kindness in his eyes which was never there for Vicki. A little amusement, too, which changed to ice as his glance shifted to enfold Vicki.

'Miss Morris has only just arrived,' he drawled. 'She couldn't think of leaving yet.'

'No, of course not.' Vicki, suddenly remembering her manners, flushed uncomfortably. 'If you like—Leoda, I can show you to your room?'

Leoda managed to look weary most charmingly. 'To tell the truth, Wade darling,' she purred, 'I do feel rather tired. I could do with a wash and perhaps a tiny rest before dinner.'

'Naturally,' he agreed sympathetically.

'What about your grandfather, though?' Leoda's brow creased as she nodded towards old Mr McLeod who had resumed dozing in his chair. 'Shouldn't I have a talk with him first?'

'No.' Wade had exchanged a brief nod with the Old Man but not much else. 'You go on upstairs. He'll hear more than enough from me. You can take your turn tomorrow. Or after dinner, if he doesn't go to bed.'

On the way upstairs Leoda said to Vicki, 'You really don't have to show me to my room, you know. I've stayed here too often not to know where it is.'

'It doesn't matter. I was coming up, anyway.' Why did she feel Leoda Morris was laughing at her? Tilting up her chin, Vicki spoke evenly, trying not to let her agitation show. 'I'll see you at dinner, then. I hope you'll soon feel better.'

'I will.' Leoda's laughter tinkled like glass chips. 'I'm not that exhausted. Wade looked after me so well on the way here.'

Miss Webb caught up with Vicki before she reached her own room. Graham was having his tea before going to bed. 'When he's asleep I'll see to old Mr McLeod, if you like. He may intend going down for dinner, but I'll try to persuade him otherwise. From what I know of him he would only talk and drink too much, which wouldn't be good for him.'

'Oh, would you?' Vicki smiled gratefully. Nurse Webb really was a godsend. 'He has a great deal of respect for you,' she admitted generously. 'If anyone could persuade him, you could.'

Miss Webb smiled appreciatively as she went on her way.

Gazing after her, Vicki felt guilty for leaving so much to her. She was about to call and say she could see to one of them when she remembered they had a guest and there was dinner to cook. Tonight she couldn't leave that to Misilgoe, and she couldn't be in two places at once. Naturally Wade would consider Miss Morris more important than either his grandfather or Graham. He wouldn't thank her if Miss Morris had to eat a burnt meal, as they had done the last time she had left the cooking entirely to the servant girls. That had been a major disaster.

In her room Vicki sat for a few minutes trying to plan the best thing to do. She tried also to subdue the terrible ache in her heart. This, she realised, wouldn't interest Wade nearly as much as the way he affected Miss Morris. If Miss Morris were to suffer any emotional distress no doubt he would be very willing to offer comfort!

Shaking herself out of her painful lethargy, Vicki took a quick shower and put on a long dress. Old Mr McLeod was very adamant over dressing for dinner and it was a custom Wade seemed disposed to continue. Sometimes she would just as soon have dined in her jeans at the kitchen table, but had soon learned that this was frowned on. It was something she had found rather confusing when she had first come to Baccaroo, the grand formality of the evening contrasted to the more casual way of life during the day.

After zipping up her dress she brushed her hair and pinned it up to keep it out of the way before leaving her room again. It was still early, but she didn't want to risk bumping into Wade and there would be too much to see to later for there to be any time to spare to change. She could always put on an overall.

This way she had hoped to escape seeing Wade upstairs, before dinner, but to her dismay she met him at the turn of the corridor before going down.

'That was quick!' As she slid to a gasping halt, his eyes swept her closely, his mouth curling at the corners as his quick glance took in her disinclination to so much as speak to him. 'So you didn't wait to welcome me home in private?'

She flushed at his sarcasm but retorted coldly, 'I can't think we have anything to say to each other—in private!'

'It wasn't a lengthy speech I had in mind,' he said harshly.

Vicki flinched as if he had struck her and her face paled. 'Since you now have Miss Morris you can't possibly want me.'

'Allow me to judge who and what I want,' he grated, his mouth hard. 'And leave Leoda out of this. Sometimes a man gets tired of struggling, and you've made it very plain you have no use for me yourself.'

He mustn't know her, she thought with dull gratitude, to say that! Her own words, she decided desperately, must be a lot nearer the truth. 'You left me in no doubt that you didn't want me either.'

He came closer, so she could see the lines etched deeply across his forehead, the glinting anger in the depth of his dark eyes as they met hers. 'I don't mind you,' he replied insolently, 'when there's nothing else available—and before you start throwing that lethal little fist of yours about, remember I warned you I won't take that lying down any more.'

If she couldn't hit out at him one way there had to be another. Vicki's slender body tensed with sudden fury. It just wasn't possible she could allow him to stand there, jeering at her, without finding some means of retaliation, of hitting him where it hurt most.

Her eyes sparkled up at him, sapphire orbs of definite beauty, set in the flushed pink of her face. 'You've been gone almost two weeks. Two weeks in a place like this, carrying huge numbers of stock, almost a hundred men. Can you wonder if I'm tense!'

'You had Jeff.'

His utter calmness infuriated her to foolish lengths. 'Of course I had Jeff!' she almost screamed, 'and I don't know what I'd have done without him, but he could have done with your advice. He told me so himself ...'

'I see,' silkily, as she paused. 'What else has he been telling you, I wonder? That you've turned into an elegant young queen? That neither he nor a lot of my other men can keep their eyes off you? That you curve too much in all the right places yet remain as slender and as supple as a young willow? That your hair floats on the breeze like waves of sunshine? Don't think I've taken leave of my senses,' he sneered, 'it's just what I've read in Jeff's eyes.' He grasped her arm, as she half crumbled with tense shock, and the cruelty of his grip couldn't be questioned. 'Is it just his eyes he can't keep off you?'

'You're despicable!'

'You've said that so often I don't hear it any more. It even makes your voice tremble. Anything you deny is a sheer waste of time!'

'I realise that. Like water off a duck's back!'

'If that's one of your more refined pommy sayings, I don't get it, but maybe you'll understand this.'

Before she could guess his intention he had jerked her to

him, so that her eyes widened with stunned surprise. The way in which he dragged her against his hard chest was ruthless, but nothing to the purpose behind his mouth. It was too much. He gave her no chance, as the savage, bruising pressure of his lips forced hers apart, to respond. Utterly shaken, she felt the havoc their impact was making throughout her whole body, but could do nothing about it. It was like being crushed by a strength and weight vastly superior to her own, but she was more frightened of the sensuous current which seemed to link them than by any physical damage he might do.

When he released her she swayed, putting a hand carefully over her hurt mouth, but as she opened wide, dazed eyes, the wild clamour of her pulses triumphed over the fluttering apprehension of her nerves.

Wade looked so uncaring of any damage he might have wrought, so immune to any emotional disturbance himself that she shivered. Quickly, fleetingly she closed her eyes again, hoping he wouldn't notice how easily he could reduce her to such a state.

Unfortunately she wasn't quick enough. His sharp glance pierced her small secrets before she could hide them and there was no mercy in the tight set of his mouth. 'That might teach you to show a little more enthusiasm when I return after an absence of almost two weeks. It's about time I started dealing out a few reprisals.'

'How did you expect me to welcome you,' she whispered, staring at him, 'after everything you've done and said? Ours isn't a normal marriage. I don't belong here.'

Wade said curtly, his eyes black, as they so often were when she said something to arouse his displeasure, 'You'd better get down to the kitchen. Maybe that's where you really belong!'

It was bewildering that, having left her abruptly with such a callous remark, he should appear in the kitchen a couple of hours later, just when dinner was almost ready to serve. Misilgoe and Boalere stood back respectfully but with dimpling smiles as he walked in, superbly handsome in his dark jacket and tie. He looked vital, intensely male and very well groomed. Nothing spared, tonight, to impress Leoda Morris, Vicki thought dully, clutching a tea-towel as if her life depended on it, her small face white.

She was unhappily aware that by contrast her own dishevelled appearance had little to commend it, but stiffened involuntarily against the derisive remarks she fully expected would be forthcoming. A meal, she was ready to retort, especially a special one, couldn't be prepared and cooked without considerable effort. And they didn't have Mrs Clover any more.

Her mouth was still bruised. She wished it had been smaller, then Wade wouldn't have noticed. Because notice he did. He came nearer, his eyes trained on it, with satisfaction in their glinting depths.

Brute, she thought dismally.

There was also satisfaction in the grunt he gave as he deliberately dipped a finger into the sauce she had just made and tasted it. Her ears pricked with astonishment as he said laconically, 'You're a superb little cook, Vicki, but I dislike you wasting your energy in a kitchen.'

'Someone has to do it!' She fell back sullenly on the age-old cry of women.

'Granted,' he wasn't impressed, 'but not my wife!'

The arrogance of the man! Vicki's eyes flashed. 'You must know women all over the world have to turn their hand to all sorts of things nowadays, and willingly.'

'So I believe,' he agreed, without relenting, 'but my wife doesn't—except in an emergency. And I think this one's gone on long enough.'

'How do you mean?'

'Let me enlighten you, Vicki.' His voice was softer but the hint of steel still there. 'When I was in Sydney I consulted an agency regarding the kind of housekeeper we need. I went to a great deal of trouble to find exactly the right woman. She'll be arriving in time for Christmas.'

'You never asked me!' Vicki knew her voice sounded strange, but the fright behind it wasn't disguised easily.

'There was no point in asking your advice,' he rejoined coldly.

Her advice! Oh, yes, she got the message! She bit her lip hard and winced. She would probably be gone before Christmas. It would be Léoda Morris he had in mind. Leoda's elegant white hands had obviously never been acquainted with a kitchen sink, nor the task of preparing a delectable dinner!'

'I see.' Vicki turned to rescue her vegetables. Leoda Morris, if she became Wade's second wife, would certainly need someone to do this kind of thing for her.

Wade took a step nearer, then moved back, as if resisting the impulse to take hold of her. 'Sometimes,' he muttered tersely, 'you see less than a blind man. Now will you please take off that absurd apron—one of Mrs Clover's if I'm not mistaken—and come with me? You look as if you could do with a drink, and we have a guest, remember!'

Old Mr McLeod had listened to Miss Webb's persuasions and gone to bed, but there was Jeff and a cousin of his, a cattle buyer who had just flown in, so the conversation was fairly general. The buyer was there to look over a few hundred head of shorthorns which Wade had brought from the Victoria River region the year before to fatten. Some stations, Vicki understood, only raised their cattle to three- or four-year-old stores and sold them to fattening properties in other areas. Wade both bred and fattened but, listening to the men talking, she realised that fattening properties were too few. When she had first come to Baccaroo, Vicki had been amazed to learn that cattle often spent weeks being driven through inadequately watered country before arriving at the fattening areas, footsore and thin. Then, after taking a year or two to recuperate, they had often to be walked many miles to the slaughtering centres in the south, or to the railheads, as many of the properties were so huge they couldn't be reached by roads. Vicki, who had thought such cattle driving expeditions had gone out with the Wild West, had been startled.

She noticed that Leoda Morris soon looked terribly bored.

'I've heard it so many times before, my dear,' she drawled, when Vicki glanced at her uncertainly. 'Don't get me wrong, though. Hundreds of women on cattle stations share this terrible enthusiasm for heat and dust and cattle. I just don't happen to be made that way. Away from the city I get bored. Of course Baccaroo is something special.' Her eyes lingered on Wade before returning coldly to Vicki. 'I could easily be tempted to spend much of my life here.'

Vicki went hot and found the rest of her meal tasted like sawdust. Leoda's meaning couldn't be mistaken, but what sort of wife would she make for Wade? Surely a station owner's wife couldn't absolutely isolate herself in the house and gardens, however luxurious they might be? Besides, Baccaroo, though comfortable, could never be termed glamorous. Vicki liked it as it was and it would take a lot of money to bring it up to Leoda Morris's standards. Then, recalling Wade's remarks in the kitchen, she realised he must be wealthy enough to pander to Miss Morris's every whim, to keep her in the idle luxury to which she was obviously accustomed. For her he might even be prepared to spend some part of every year in the city.

Secretly she watched him, feeling childish when he caught her at it but not able to look away when his grey eyes studied hers. She could read little in them. She was so busy trying to that she forgot her own might be unconsciously revealing. She found herself longing that things might have been different between them. If only theirs could have been a normal marriage! Then she could happily have welcomed his return as—what had he said?—a normal wife would. Wouldn't it have been truly wonderful to have been able to throw her arms around him in front of everyone, especially Miss Morris! But of course, he hadn't meant she should go that far when he had talked of her welcome being lukewarm.

Miss Webb spoke, just as Vicki felt she might be drowning in eyes which held hers unashamedly captive. 'Graham is delighted with his present, Mr McLeod.'

His present? Vicki felt sudden tears sting her eyes before she wrenched her gaze from his—not before a little of her anguish showed but soon enough, she hoped, to save her pride. He had brought his son a present but not his wife. Any vague hopes she had had that things might change between them faded. This only seemed to emphasise the way things were going.

The buyer filled the brief silence with stories of his own sons, ending with a humorous remark directed at Jeff that if he didn't hurry up and marry he was going to be left out.

'Maybe the woman I want just isn't available,' Jeff appeared to surprise even himself by saying tautly, his glance sliding involuntarily towards Vicki.

Vicki heard herself replying, utterly without intention, her reaction to despair immediate, perhaps as she was so familiar with it herself. 'One day she could be, Jeff. Very soon ...' She wanted to go on, but Wade's look silenced her.

'It happens to the best of us, Jeff,' he said forcibly, and changed the subject deliberately. But not before Vicki felt the full impact of his icy disapproval.

Jeff was distracted, though doing his best to hide it, realising he had overstepped the mark with Wade, but not even his quick, apologetic glance made Vicki feel much better. The buyer's eyes were curious and Leoda Morris's spitefully alert. Vicki, for no good reason she could think of, only wanted to sink through the floor.

Later Wade went out with the other two men and, surprisingly, Leoda decided to retire. She had had a headache all day and it was after eleven. She went upstairs followed

by a sympathetic and obviously impressed Miss Webb
who advised her gently on the excellence of a hot drink and
aspirin.

Vicki, feeling ashamed of being reluctant to add her own
administrations to those of Miss Webb, stayed behind a
few minutes before going up herself. Not wanting to stay
down long enough to hear Wade's possible comments on
her earlier indiscretions, she almost ran to her room.

Just as quickly she undressed and got into her narrow
bed, wishing feverishly that she had some sleeping tablets.
She had been sleeping badly and tonight she had no desire
to lie awake, to hear Wade pause enquiringly outside Leoda
Morris's door. Technically she knew she couldn't as it was
too far away, but in her mind she could see it clearly. He
would stop and knock. She would open the door and let him
in, welcome him with a devastating smile, her headache
forgotten.

Trying desperately to bolt out the agony it aroused,
Vicki turned and buried her head in her pillow.

# CHAPTER TEN

FIVE minutes later Vicki was still lying there when Wade came in. She heard the door open, not too gently, and his decisive footsteps coming over the floor. It could only be him; she didn't look up as he paused by her bed. As she had done before, she pretended to be asleep, hoping he might go away. What she had said to Jeff was probably reprehensible but hadn't been premeditated, and she didn't feel she need apologise.

She didn't realise the utter stillness of her body betrayed her. Wade placed a far from kind hand on her bare shoulder, jerking her over to face him.

'You could suffocate lying like that.' He spoke coldly, but his eyes were smouldering flames when she looked up at him.

Feeling instantly that she had some reason to defend herself, she tried to forestall what she knew instinctively was coming. 'I didn't expect to see you.'

'You never do, do you?' His mouth thinned as he stared down at her. 'You make the most outrageously obvious remarks and expect me to take them lying down!'

'I'm sorry,' she muttered, aware that an apology might be necessary, yet unwilling to take the entire blame. Hard misery caught at her heart and brought a quick shudder. 'But if I did precipitate matters a little, you can't really blame me. You never made any secret of your intentions to be rid of me as soon as possible.'

'Not so you can live with Jeff, right under my nose!'

'I'll live where I like!' Why did she feel sick at even the thought of leaving Wade? 'Not that I imagine for one moment that I'd want to stay here.'

'You can't think I'd let you? Carrying on your clandestine meetings, your secret assignments . . .'

'That's a lie!' she spat at him, no docile, anguished young girl any more, wilting under his hard attack, but a small, spitting cat. 'At least Jeff Curry's good and kind and doesn't parade his other women in front of me and ask me to entertain them! You couldn't wait to get rid of me before bringing Leoda Morris back here. You'll be off to her room, I suppose, now that you've lectured me on the crime of being unfaithful!'

'Be quiet, damn you!'

She didn't obey, not even when his eyes struck such sparks they seemed to burn her. Her voice did waver fractionally but gained momentum. She was unable to stop. 'I remember how I caught you coming out of her room in the middle of the night!'

'You little fool—you don't know what you're talking about!' His control was taking greater effort now. This much was clear as his hands bit deeper into her smooth arms, but Vicki, her head thrown back, the vivid colour coming and going in her satiny cheeks, was past taking heed of any danger signals.

'I have the evidence of my own eyes!' she cried, drunk with a reckless resentment. 'It's not just some gossip I listened to. I'm not putting two and two together and making six, as you're doing!'

'So you've decided I'm going to her tonight?'

Her heart beginning to beat rapidly, Vicki realised she had driven him somewhere beyond his normal iron limits of restraint. 'Just leave me,' she gasped, with an optimism which died almost before it was born.

Before she could move, with a swift exclamation, he was picking her up and carrying her through to his room. His arms were tight around her struggling body, his face carved like granite above the ivory paleness of her own. Then she was on his bed with his tall length stretched out beside her and he was kissing her with angry, almost brutal kisses while his merciless hands tore her brief nightclothes from the shrinking softness of her limbs.

'No, Wade, no! I can't bear it!' she spoke in quick little gasps against his punishing mouth.

'You're going to have to bear a lot more than this,' he rasped, his mouth leaving hers only long enough to enable him to throw off the loose towelling robe he wore.

'How you must hate me!' Her lips parted as her breathing quickened. 'I never hated you,' she moaned, turning her head in a futile effort to avoid him, not knowing why she was confessing even this much.

'You might before morning,' he said thickly, using his hand to turn her back to him, his body half over hers to hold her still. 'I mean to have you and if another man cares to take my leavings then he's welcome. You might also, come the morning, be convinced I didn't spend the night in another woman's bed.'

'No, Wade—you must listen!' She was struggling now in earnest as fear lent her strength. 'That's not the only thing! You want a divorce, don't you? This way you could be ruining your chances.'

'Have you quite finished?' Impassively his arms finally prevented further frantic struggles from her small, quivering body, his muscular legs aiding his control of her slender limbs. It was terrifying that she could only lie panting against him and that she seemed to be arousing him to the point where reason departed. Yet with the exquisite cruelty of his complete dominance she could feel her own senses beginning to respond fiercely.

He appeared about to go on castigating her, then changed his mind as he expertly judged how she sought to hide her stormy response. 'Let's call a truce for a few hours,' he groaned against her breast. 'I want you, Vicki! I wouldn't be telling the truth if I denied it. I can make you want me just as much, but I want to hear you say so. I want to hear you admit it.'

'It's just sex,' she gasped, twisting her head this way and that to avoid his seeking mouth, which she knew might soon have her speaking as wildly as he was. 'Nothing else,' she choked. 'It's degrading!'

But her lips were trembling with a warmth of uncertainty and passion as he stopped her feverish flow of defensive words. His mouth crushed hers until reality faded and she could only cling to him, unable to defend the crumbling barriers she had erected so weakly against his superior male strength. His mouth wandered to her closed eyes, over her hot cheeks, on down the slender column of her neck to rest on the traitorously beating pulse at its base.

It was minutes before he commented on her last wild statement. 'Whichever way you describe what's happening isn't going to make me change my mind. I don't know why I've waited so long, nor do I know why you protest so much when every bit of you is crying out to belong to me!'

'You're the one who usually knows all the answers.' Vickie could scarcely speak. It took a tremendous effort to do anything at all, all her concentration being given over to the mammoth task of resisting him, of ignoring the surging delight which threatened to consume her whole body.

'Yes,' he increased that delight by sliding his hands slowly over her taut breasts, 'but some things no longer make sense. You're going to have to find a few answers yourself, and very soon, so take warning. Right now it's sufficient to have you here in my arms, like this.'

The blood was hot through her body, singing in her veins, and she could feel his heart pounding over her own, his powerful muscles straining against her. On a sobbing breath, which despaired of her own sensuous response, she made one last effort. 'You must listen to me, Wade. You never wanted Graham ...'

'He's my son, isn't he?'

'You don't love him!'

'Vicki!' he groaned, his mouth coming back to hers again, with a hungry urgency which betrayed his impatient needs, 'leave it, will you? God, you don't know what you're doing to me. We can talk later—tomorrow.'

'No!' She tried to resist, but he simply tightened his hold, bringing her back to him, pinning her half under him so she was wholly trapped by his ruthless weight. To move was impossible, to try and do so only made her more conscious of the heat and roughness of his skin, the hardness of his fingers gripping her chin.

He trailed a hand across her throat, his lips following, before moving to her ear. 'Don't you ever listen to a thing I tell you?'

'I——' Vicki's world was exploding around her beneath the sensuous movements of his hands. She couldn't recall what she had been going to say. How could she even think with his harsh breath raging over her, his heart deafening her with its heavy, threatening beat?

'Vicki,' he said huskily, 'the memory of the last time is too vivid. I want you, the delight you can give, and I don't think either of us wants to stop now. You could try being honest for a change.'

She was intensely aware that he spoke the truth. Where he was concerned she was vulnerable, especially when she loved him. His mouth seemed to touch every bit of her trembling body before coming back to explore her parting lips. The sensuality of his kisses brought surrender swift and complete. As his hands slid over the lovely curve of her hip, her arms went tightly around his neck, her fingers seeking the hardness of his broad shoulders, clutching them with tense abandonment. Then their bodies moved together and clung until a sudden violence exploded within them, shattering the cool depth of the night about them with repetitive light, like a burning torch of a thousand flames.

In the morning Wade was still beside her, his arm around her, his body hard against hers. But when she awoke and unconsciously lifted her mouth to his, he merely pressed a swift kiss on it and immediately left her.

'Don't tempt me, I'm late already,' he said grimly. 'I have to see the buyer who came last night and there's another one flying in this afternoon. I'll see you later.'

There was something very final about the deliberate taut-
ness of his body as he went through the door. This must be
the last time, she realised, that she would ever lie here and
watch him leave like this. The last time, she reiterated,
wondering however she would survive such pain.

Through the night she imagined she'd heard him whisper something about never letting her go. But most of the
night she had been so out of her mind with loving him she
might have made a mistake. For her own sake she must only
remember how he hated her. Her wanton response to his
lovemaking would just be something he would recall with
a cynical indifference when he eventually married the
woman he loved.

After he had gone she dresed quickly and began her day,
feeling forced to go about it as if nothing had happened.
Leoda Morris grumbled continually that Wade wasn't
around to talk to, trying Vicki's stretched nerves beyond
endurance by her constant references to him. Old Mr
McLeod didn't help as he refused to see Leoda for even a
few minutes.

Mr McLeod was another worry this morning. For the
first time Vicki could remember he declined to get up. It
was this more than anything else which threw her into a
mild panic and caused her to tackle him about it. While
aware that an almost imperceptible friendship had grown
between them she hadn't realised how fond she had become
of him. Yet when she asked he simply said he felt a little
tired.

Miss Webb, with her expert knowledge of nursing, was
convinced there was nothing to get in a state about, but
Vicki was not so sure. Wade had disappeared to the far
reaches of the property and probably wouldn't be home until nightfall. While feeling she might be accused of making
the wrong decision, Vicki decided not to call the flying doctor. Wade would know what to do.

As if this was not enough, more problems demanding a
decision arose after lunch. An old friend of the McLeods',

with a large station south of Alice, was in touch to remind Vicki that she had promised to bring Graham and his nurse over for the afternoon. She had forgotten all about it, perhaps because of old Mr McLeod. Feeling she couldn't possibly leave him, and with Graham almost dancing with disappoinment, she asked Leoda if she would go instead.

Fortunately a bored Leoda was delighted and, after seeing them off, Vicki went to sit with the Old Man, by his bedside.

Thinking to amuse him a little, she mentioned how excited Graham had become over his outing. Then she touched on his growing love for Baccaroo, how well he was settling down. It didn't hurt her to say so any more and she understood the comfort the Old Man derived from hearing it.

This afternoon, however, he astonished her almost to speechlessness by a curtly asked question. 'How would it be if I told you to take the boy and leave, at the first chance?'

Vicki stared at him, unable to believe her ears. 'You can't really mean that, Mr McLeod!'

'Yes.' He looked drawn and worried, vulnerable—if that wasn't so impossible. 'Damn it all, child, I was responsible for bringing you back and I know, when I'm gone, Wade intends to keep the boy.'

'Keep Graham ... ?' She felt bewildered, not knowing how much the Old Man knew, how much it was safe to say.

'Yes,' the Old Man shook his white head. 'I shouldn't be telling you this, but Wade told me last night, while I believe you were cooking dinner. Said he wouldn't let the boy go, not ever.'

Vicki hesitated, struck by shock, scarcely able to ascertain what this could mean. 'Wade must have been saying this to reassure you?'

'No, I asked him.'

'But ...'

'You see, my dear,' he said quietly, 'I've known all along that Wade was only willing to keep the boy while I was still alive. So you see there was no reason why he should pretend.'

'He still could be!'

'No, child, I know Wade.'

She drew a deep aching breath. 'Did he mention me?'

Again the Old Man shook his head. 'I'm sorry, Victoria, he did not. That's why I want you to take the boy and go. It will just about break my heart, but it won't kill me, so don't look so worried. I'll arrange everything.'

Her heart was full of such compassion for the Old Man that she could not speak, but she knew it was not just for his sake she said 'no'.

'No?' He had to lean forward to hear her anguished whisper. 'Why not?'

'I can't.' Vicki's face was white, but her voice was stronger, although every bit of light had gone from her eyes. 'You see, I love Wade, Mr McLeod. If he really loves Graham and wants him I couldn't take his son from him. when the time comes I'll simply disappear again. Somehow I'll find the strength.'

'You'll never do it, child.'

'That's what you don't understand.' Vicki stared at him desperately. 'I'm not a child any more, Mr McLeod. You think I'm being childish, too dramatic. I know I maybe sound this way, but I love Wade so much I'll be able to make any sacrifice.'

'You're sure?'

She turned her face, tear-streaked but resolute, towards him. 'Both Wade and Graham belong here, Mr McLeod. I might have done, but Wade never really wanted me. But it's because I care so much that I'll find the strength to do this. Besides, how could I deprive Graham of his rightful inheritance? What could I ever offer to compare with Baccaroo? Already he loves it. Perhaps, in the years ahead, Wade might let me see him.'

'Vicki!' Wade was standing in the doorway.

Vicki had always read that, on occasions like this, one usually spun round on a whirl of fright, but she was so shocked she couldn't move. Her back was to the door. How long had he been there? Surely he had just arrived? He couldn't have heard anything.

Numbly she stared at the Old Man, her eyes wide, her tears unheeded. The Old Man himself, after one sharp glance at both of them, slumped back on his pillows and closed his eyes. 'I've already told you, Wade,' he mumbled, 'how fond I've grown of your wife, but as I need a rest, you can take her away, with my blessing.'

If Vicki had taken that in she might have thought it a strange thing for the Old Man to come out with. As it was she found herself in Wade's bedroom without quite realising how she got there. It must be her day for bedrooms, she decided hysterically, as she shook off Wade's propelling hands. The knowledge of his return began to sink in like a douche of cold reality, but there could be nothing for it but to brazen her way out.

'Don't you want something to eat, Wade?' Her voice shook, but she managed to control it. 'Your grandfather's been tired all day and we've been worried, especially when we couldn't get in touch with you.'

'Stop worrying.' His eyes glinted, with only so much tolerance. 'He does take to his bed for the odd day. He hasn't done recently, not since you came, so you wouldn't know about it.'

She looked around helplessly. 'I don't know why you brought me here. Your buyers?'

'They've gone. That is, one has. I cancelled the other. Misilgoe told me that Graham and the two women have gone visiting, so the house is empty and it's going to be quite a while before I want anything to eat—if at all. It rather depends on you.'

'Wade?' Vicki could bear it no longer. Her eyes sought an answer to the question she dared not put into words.

Had he overheard what she had said to his grandfather?

He stared back at her darkly, then pushed her gently on to the edge of the bed, coming down beside her himself but not touching her. He kept his eyes on her suddenly averted profile, as she clasped her hands tightly together and bent her head, her apprehensive gaze fixed on them.

When he spoke this time it was harshly. 'I returned early, Vicki, because I couldn't keep away from you, much as I tried. I knew we had to talk and tonight was suddenly too long to wait. I had to ask you to stay with me and the waiting was doing things to me I didn't like.'

He paused, but she was too stunned and bewildered to find even the strength to lift her bowed head. She felt slightly sick, hitting the depth of humiliation as she realised Wade must have heard her declaring her undying love for him! Couldn't she have been spared that?

He must have sensed her despair, but that didn't stop him. She almost cried out when he asked grimly, 'Was it true what I heard you telling the Old Man, that you love me?'

What could she do, after unbearable seconds had passed, but nod slowly? Though her pride was in shreds she couldn't lie! Not that it really mattered any more. Now Wade was probably about to pour contempt on her head for being willing to part with Graham, but not even this seemed to stop her from whispering, 'Yes, I do love you.'

Whatever she expected it wasn't to be seized in his arms in a grip which almost hurt. Regardless of her startled cry, she was caught and crushed to him, held against him as if he never intended letting her go.

Thickly he said, 'How long have you known?'

Tears half choked her voice, but she managed to say agonisingly, 'I think soon after I married you. When I first came back again to Baccaroo, I thought I'd changed.'

'Yes?' he prompted, the muscles of his hard jaw noticeably tense as she hesitated.

Why, Vicky wondered bitterly, was he making her

confess all this? Surely he wasn't adding torture to the long list of weapons he could use against her. He held her, and against hers his body was tense, but this didn't mean he cared for her. With an acid taste in her mouth, she exclaimed. 'I discovered I still loved you, but it was different.'

'How—different?'

Did he have to wring it so ruthlessly from her! Burying her hot face against him, every inch of her protesting, she muttered desperately, 'I think I'd grown up, while I was away. My feelings for you aren't childishly uncertain any more. They're purely adult, and they hurt.'

Suddenly he was kissing her, his mouth coming down on hers with a fierceness of possession which took her breath away. He was hurting her, but she clung to him, knowing it was a fatal reaction but no longer able to take heed of her pride. Let him read what he liked in her headlong response. It wasn't possible now that he didn't realise the depth of her feelings, but she was past all sensible caring. These few moments in his arms, the savage violence of his kisses, might be the last she would have to store against the bleakness of a future without him.

When he spoke, so unhappy were her thoughts, she couldn't believe she was hearing properly. 'God, Vicki, never run away again as you did after I first learnt about Graham! I never want to suffer again like that! I'd given up all hope of making you love me, but since the first moment I saw you I knew you were going to mean something in my life. I never visualised loving you so desperately, though. I never knew I was capable of feeling as I do about anyone, never mind a small scrap of a girl scarcely higher than my heart.' The whiteness of his face betraying his feelings even more than the thickness of his voice, he buried his face in her silken cloud of hair.

Completely dazed, Vicki eased back from him a little, trying to take in the dazzling fact that he must love her, yet unable to stop her mind going off at a tangent. The hard pain in his face was more than she could bear. 'Wade,' she faltered, 'I understand—a lot more than you think. Mrs Clover did explain ...'

'What made me what I am, you mean?' His mouth hardened grimly, 'I know you knew some of it. The Old Man and I must have seemed a very formidable pair to someone like you?'

'Mrs Clover told me,' Vicki felt forced to take a deep breath, 'about your mother dying—your father—well, almost everything.'

'But that was no reason to treat you as I did,' he exclaimed savagely, his eyes black. 'When I asked you to marry me I never stopped to consider your actual feelings. When I began to find you more attractive and couldn't resist you, I was convinced I could have you without it making much difference in either of our lives. That morning, when I found you ill in the bathroom and realised what was wrong, I reacted furiously, but it was partly from shock. I accused you, my darling, of many things to hide my own guilt.'

Vicki, who had never dreamt of hearing him speak like this, felt her eyes widen. His humility might only be fleeting but, while it lasted, it was like a balm. 'You told me to go.'

'Yes,' his eyes went bleak and his arms tightened around her, 'I suppose I meant it. It wasn't until later in the day that I became aware what a complete fool I'd been. It suddenly dawned on me how much I loved you, how you meant more to me than anyone or anything else. You were my wife, the mother of my unborn son. I couldn't get home fast enough.'

His breath came harshly as he stared at her, 'When I reached Baccaroo and found you gone I nearly went out of my head! If you don't believe it, ask Jeff, any man, woman or child on the station. I'd lost loved ones before, but it was nothing to the pain of losing you, Mrs Clover told me how she'd found you in a dead faint on the bathroom floor. I went cold then, Vicki. I think I remained that way until the day I found you.'

Uncertainly she said, 'I left as soon as I could because I didn't think you wanted to see me again. Knowing of the situation between you and your grandfather, I could understand. I thought I was doing the right thing.'

He smiled without humour, as if the memory of her leaving was still too vivid. 'There are things I'd like to know, Vickie. If I'd had any idea you loved me I would have asked as soon as you came around in hospital. As it was, I let McLeod pride get in the way again. That day you left I traced you to Darwin. You'd bought a ticket for the U.K. It made sense that you should go there, back to your native land, but I could never trace you. I went there myself and tried every means possible, but you seemed to have vanished into thin air. Back here I searched every place, every town and city I could think of before being forced to come to the grim conclusion that something had happened to you.'

A shudder, actually running through his strong, muscular body, convinced Vicki that this hard man had suffered. More than she would ever have believed. She stared at him, her face paling, as she heard him recall those days she would rather forget.

'I didn't go back to England, Wade. I bought a ticket but gave it to another girl who went instead. At the last minute I couldn't leave Australia—it was as simple as that. This was my home now, and I loved it, although I did realise, after leaving you, that I probably hadn't a friend. That same day I came south to Melbourne, the whole length of the country, and looked around for a living-in job. I did get a temporary one through a newspaper ad., but the couple were elderly and couldn't keep me until Graham was born. They had to have someone all the time, you see. However, I'd saved enough to enable me to take a room in the cheaper part of the city, the same room you found me in.'

'How did you manage until Graham was born, in a strange neighbourhood?' Wade's jaw was curiously rigid.

'Not too badly, really,' Vicki, sensing his pain, forced herself to speak lightly, to put from her any recollection of those long, lonely weeks. 'Everyone—everyone I knew, that is, was very kind. Afterwards, as you know, I got a new job with Madame Sorelle and earned enough for two.'

Wade rose to his feet as if he could sit no longer. 'When the Suttons spotted you at the agricultural show and told the Old Man I was stunned, but not half as much as I was when we actually found you.' He turned, taking hold of her, pulling her into his arms as if he couldn't bear to let her go, even for a minute. Crushing her to him again, he muttered hoarsely, 'My God, Vicki, never in my life have I felt so bad! I've had my moments of deliberate silence, but never before have I been reduced to the state of being unable to speak. Seeing you, after years of not knowing whether you were dead or alive, was like having someone kick me where it hurt most. I wanted to shout and curse, I wanted to cry—yes, a grown man! I felt I was quite capable of doing what I could scarcely recall being weak enough to do, even as a child. I wanted to pick you up and kiss away all the terrible things you must obviously have endured—for which I'd been responsible. My son was there and, like the Old Man, I was moved beyond everything when I looked at him. Yet you were by far the more important. I still loved you, my darling, more than ever, if that was possible, but my hands, because of my own actions, seemed tied. I thought you must hate me and that any show of passion would only make you more frightened than you already were.'

Tears were streaming down Vicki's cheeks, she wasn't able to stop them. 'I wish I'd known!' she whispered.

'While you were in hospital,' he said soberly, 'I was able to kiss you, when you didn't know me.'

'I felt someone had kissed me when I woke, but you

were so harsh, so like a stranger, I thought I must have been dreaming. Wade,' she said softly, as his mouth lowered gently to kiss away her tears, 'why did you allow your grandfather to bring Graham back here? And why did you insist I come too but that we both must leave again after your grandfather died?'

Wade shook his head, staring at her with a little of his old arrogance. 'I'm not sure, my darling, and that's the truth. Maybe, through loving you, I'd learnt compassion. I came to realise that the Old Man was probably more to be pitied than anything else and my long years of disliking him had achieved precisely nothing. He really does have a heart condition, as you know, but I was ready to grasp at any excuse to get you both here, my wife and my son! But a man's very vulnerable when he believes the woman he loves hates him. It seemed the only defence I had, to tell you you were free to go, after the Old Man died. I'm afraid I didn't love you all the time, either. Often I felt torn by hate because of the torture I'd suffered when you left me. I couldn't easily get rid of such black moods. They still haunted me. It must have been that that made me so harsh with you.'

'Then you would have let me go again?'

'No,' his arms tightened, 'you wouldn't have got five yards. You'll have to forgive me, child, but I've taken every precaution since you returned. You couldn't have gone anywhere without my knowledge.'

Vicki shivered at his adamant tone, her eyes bewildered. 'But you gave me such a neglected room!'

For the first time he smiled ruefully. 'Only because I didn't believe you would stay in it. I fully expected you to be creeping in here, begging to share my bed. When you did come in, that first night, I thought I'd succeeded beyond my wildest expectations. That you swiftly disillusioned me, you little hussy, was bad enough, but the realisation that things were going to take much longer to put them right than I'd hoped was infinitely worse.

If I learnt one thing from that too brief encounter it was how much I still loved and wanted you.'

Vicki stirred restlessly as his eyes slowly explored her face before slipping to her figure. She gulped, 'You must have guessed how much I wanted to stay with you that night. If I didn't put it into actual words there must have been times when I've betrayed how much I loved you? Yet when you went off to Sydney you brought another woman back with you, as you said you would!'

He replied, suddenly very severe, 'One question at a time, Vicki. I didn't know you loved me. I knew you responded to me, I wouldn't be much of a man if I hadn't been able to realise that, but sex without love can become meaningless.'

'You never encouraged my love,' she retorted bravely. 'You were never very kind.'

'I didn't feel that way, but stop interrupting,' he said dryly. 'I forgot about my threat, almost before it was uttered. The business in Sydney took longer than I expected and after it was finished I had to go to Nooanda. It was purely accidental that I bumped into Leoda in Alice as I was coming back. She was on her way here.'

'But she implied . . . ?'

He laughed. 'She's always been good at implying a lot of things which don't exist, but your openly condemning expression when we arrived didn't help much, my darling. I could read your chaste little thoughts so clearly and, although I knew I was partly responsible, I felt furious that you were so ready to judge me. That's why I didn't explain what had actually happened. Leoda's people and mine have always been friendly, but I hadn't seen her since you left. This visit will be short, and somehow I don't think we'll be seeing much of her in the future.'

Jealously, Vicki couldn't prevent herself reminding him 'I did once catch you coming from her room.'

'So you did.' His smile was teasing. 'She came knocking

on my door that night, asking for aspirins. I supplied them and escorted her back.'

'Was that all she was after?'

His eyes gleamed, 'It was all she got. She and I have never been lovers, but I warn you here and now, Vicki McLeod, I refuse to give you a run-down on all the women I've known.'

'There've been a lot?'

Laughing softly, he drew her closer, 'None at all since I married you, and you're the only one I've ever loved. I think it must have happened that first time I kissed you. There you were, standing staring at me, all huge blue eyes. I felt as if I'd committed a crime, but it was one I had a sudden urge to repeat.'

The same blue eyes grew starry. 'You won't be sending me away?'

'Oh, Vicki,' he groaned, pressing urgent kisses on her soft mouth, 'I'll never risk doing that again. My grandfather has been rough, but he's learnt to love you too. It wouldn't matter if he didn't, but it will make life easier for you, the last few weeks we have him.'

'I know,' she said quietly.

'All you have to do now, my darling, is concentrate on me. You'll have no excuse not to when your new housekeeper arrives and you have Miss Webb looking after Graham.'

In spite of the teasing glint in his eye her own clouded. 'You do care for your son, Wade?'

'Naturally,' he smiled, but his face was serious. 'I don't suppose Miss Webb has mentioned the hours she's spent gossiping with the wives while I've got to know him? I've taught him to ride and plenty of other things, I've reason to believe we're growing mutually fond of each other. My son and I, minx, in case you're again getting the wrong ideas.'

Vicki hesitated, 'I like Miss Webb, Wade. She's proved

a good friend and fits in somehow, though at first I didn't think so.' She lowered her head, trying to hide a guilty colour, 'What I'm trying to ask is—do you think she is really necessary?'

'She could be.' He looked at Vicki intently as his arms urged her back against the pillows. 'Maybe,' he added gently teasing, 'she might soon have two to look after?'

Hiding her face against him, Vicki didn't shake her head, and when he lifted her chin to examine her flushed cheeks she couldn't deny it.

'Never mind,' his voice was still soft, if slightly thicker, his hand gentle as he ran it over her shining hair, 'I've discovered you love me and the rest will follow in due time. I want you to myself for a little while, to teach you how to belong to me completely, as surely as I belong to you.'

The afternoon sun dimmed as Vicki turned her mouth up to his with a sigh of surrender and undisguised longing. The wind outside was rising, but she was only conscious of the tall man beside her. Loving him dearly, she laced slender young arms around his neck, holding him ever closer. If this was happiness, at last, she could find no fault with it!

# *Harlequin* Plus

## A WORD ABOUT THE AUTHOR

Margaret Pargeter was born in the quiet Northumbrian Valley, in the extreme northeast of England, where she lives today.

When did she first feel an urge to write? "Truthfully, I can't recall," she admits. "It must have been during my early teens. I remember carrying a notebook in my pocket, and while milking cows I would often take a break to scribble something down."

The jottings developed into short stories, and Margaret's first break came several years after she had married. Her husband talked her into entering a writing contest, and her work caught the eye of an editor, who asked her to write serial stories. From there she went on to complete her first romance novel, *Winds from the Sea* (Romance #1899).

Among the author's many blessings, which she likes to keep counting, is the "pleasure I get from knowing that people enjoy reading my books. And," she adds, "I hope they long continue to do so."

# SUPERROMANCE
## SUBSCRIPTION
## RESERVATION COUPON

 Complete and mail TODAY to

---

### Harlequin Reader Service

In the U.S.A.
1440 South Priest Drive
Tempe, AZ 85281

In Canada
649 Ontario Street
Stratford, Ontario N5A 6W2

Please reserve my subscription to the 2 NEW
SUPERROMANCES published every eight weeks
(12 a year). Every eight weeks I will receive
2 NEW SUPERROMANCES at the low price of
$2.50 each (total— $5). There are no shipping and
handling or any other hidden charges, and I am free
to cancel at any time after taking as many or
as few novels as I wish.

NAME_____
(Please Print)

ADDRESS_____

CITY_____

STATE/PROV._____

ZIP/POSTAL CODE_____

Offer expires January 31, 1982.                     BP453
Prices subject to change without notice